October, 1961

To Ghislaine Goderme
with warm
greetings
and high
regard
from

Lawrence S. Kubie

PRACTICAL AND THEORETICAL
ASPECTS OF PSYCHOANALYSIS

PRACTICAL AND THEORETICAL ASPECTS OF PSYCHOANALYSIS

By LAWRENCE S. KUBIE

FREDERICK A. PRAEGER, *Publishers*

NEW YORK

BOOKS THAT MATTER

Published in the United States of America in 1960
by Praeger Paperbacks, Inc.
64 University Place, New York 3, N. Y.

The original edition of this book
was published in 1950
by International Universities Press, Inc.
The present edition contains some revisions
and new material.

Library of Congress catalog card number 60-15702

Manufactured in the United States of America

To
Analytic Patients Everywhere,
to their Families and Medical Advisers,
and to my Colleagues

CONTENTS

FOREWORD

When this book was published in 1950, it represented both
a revision and an expansion of its predecessor, which had been
published in 1934 under the briefer title *Practical Aspects of
Psychoanalysis*. Now, for this newest edition, further material
has been added and revised to bring the work up to date.

In the more than twenty-five years since my book first
appeared, higher standards for specialists have been established in every field of medical science. In 1934, there were
no official steps by which a physician could be certified as
a specialist in any field; there were no "specialty boards" to
enforce minimal standards of training or minimal years of
experience, to be followed by rigorous examinations; there
was no way in which post-doctoral training in a specialty
could be evaluated or given official recognition. Since then,
standards and procedures have been set up in every aspect
of medical science and practice.

Specialization in neurology and psychiatry is under the
supervision of the American Board of Psychiatry, which
gives no special recognition, however, to psychoanalytic training as a sub-specialty. Consequently, the acknowledgment
that a psychiatrist has the right to call himself a psychoanalyst has depended not upon certification by the American
Board, but upon the completion of training in one of the
institutes or training centers which has been accepted by the
American Psychoanalytic Association as a school for the
training of psychoanalysts. The satisfactory completion of
training is implied by graduation, by election to membership
in an affiliated psychoanalytic society, and by subsequent
election to membership in the American Psychoanalytic Association. In effect, this has been equivalent to certification as
a specialist.

The central problem has been to maintain high standards

of training and at the same time to avoid the danger of rigidity. The existing system has allowed for a reasonable degree of flexibility, while limiting the tendency of all organizations to impede healthy change. Local theories and techniques might vary, and standards in some centers might be less exacting than in others; but none could be too far out of line. Now being considered is the advisability of instituting a system of certification in psychoanalysis by an American Board of Psychoanalysis, which would be a subdivision of the American Board of Psychiatry. Men would be eligible for this only after they had been certified as specialists in psychiatry, with full psychoanalytic training. This would superimpose a special certification in psychoanalysis upon the more general certification in psychiatry. The plan may or may not be adopted; but the mere fact that it is being considered is an indication of the growing importance of psychoanalysis in psychiatric education.

Certain noteworthy achievements have marked the development of psychiatry and psychoanalysis in this country over the past twenty-five years. Psychoanalytic psychiatry has penetrated beyond medical education into many aspects of cultural, sociological, anthropological, and educational thinking. In many medical centers, psychoanalytic psychiatry is used as an investigative instrument in medical, surgical, and specialty wards, and in out-patient dispensaries. Psychoanalytic thinking has also invaded neurophysiological and neurobiochemical research; and this interpenetration has moved in both directions. Among trained psychoanalysts are men who are also working on the anatomy, physiology, biochemistry, and pharmacology of the nervous system. In short, a remarkable integration of psychoanalytic and physiological thinking has occurred in clinical work, in research, and in the organization of medical education. There is a growing recognition of the fact that all human behavior represents the confluence of individual experience, of cultural processes, and of biophysical and biochemical processes. The behavioral scientist today rejects any unilateral approach to the problems of human behavior.

Also, in the twenty-five years since the first edition of this book appeared, the membership of the American Psychoanalytic Association has grown to 850, with 900 students in 18 institutes and training centers scattered throughout the country (see Appendix).

With this growth, the isolation of psychoanalysis which marked and marred its development in Europe is ceasing; but as psychoanalysis becomes less and less isolated, we are challenged increasingly to re-examine its many premises. In the final chapter of this book, a few of the current areas of re-examination will be listed.

INTRODUCTION

For the prospective patient this book can serve four immediate needs.

(1) Avoidable Misunderstandings

The progress of an analysis can be assisted by a sound intellectual understanding between the psychoanalyst, the patient, the patient's family, and the physician who has sent the patient to the psychoanalyst. It is not to be expected, however, that such an intellectual rapport will eliminate all emotional obstacles. Logical exposition can dispel only those fears which are based on misunderstanding and misrepresentation. Others have deeper roots which can be altered only by the process of analysis itself. Nor is it desirable that frank and open skepticism should be suppressed. Credulity is at least as destructive to the therapeutic efficacy of an analysis as is open rebellion. Misunderstandings about facts, however, whether among laymen or within the medical profession, serve no constructive purpose; and it is hoped that this book will help to eliminate at least those unnecessary misconceptions which arise when people are merely misinformed.

(2) The Relationship of Doctor and Patient in Analysis

The introduction of the psychoanalytic method at first brought no significant alterations in the traditional relationship between the patient and his physician. Gradually, however, certain modifications occurred in this age-old bond. These changes have been a necessary outcome of experience; but it is natural that they should often be misunderstood. A simple explanation of this changed relationship may remove the undesirable atmosphere of mystery and distrust which sometimes seems to surround the practice of psychoanalysis, and should make possible a closer working rapport among the analyst, the referring physician, the patient, and the patient's family.

(3) Help in Selecting a Psychoanalyst

In all fields of medicine the layman has to take a physician's competence largely on faith. Indeed the popular reputation of any practitioner has an almost accidental relationship to his scientific ability. The layman forms his estimate of a physician chiefly through his emotional response to the physician's personality, plus the legends which grow up about his supposed therapeutic successes and failures. In any field of medical practice these at best are misleading guides; and this is especially true in psychoanalysis. In the first place, the better the analyst the less does he play up his personality, for reasons which will be discussed below. Second, the symptoms of neurotic illness are often intrinsically obscure. Third, neurotic patients often hide their ills even from their nearest friends and relations, and not infrequently from their physicians as well. Finally, even when they are willing to talk freely about their symptoms, once they are in the midst of treatment patients can usually describe very little of what goes on. How then can a layman judge the ability of an unknown and reticent analyst from the results of the mysterious treatment of some friend whose troubles he recognizes only vaguely if at all? How, then, can the ability of a psychoanalyst be judged from his work? Fortunately, as will be explained below, there are ways of ascertaining at least the training and the formal professional competence of any man who claims to be an analyst, and so of eliminating some of the more serious mistakes which can occur in the search for analytic help.

(4) The Deluge of Questions

There is hardly a day in the social or professional life of an analyst, or of a patient under analysis, in which he is not asked a multitude of questions, such as: "What is psychoanalysis about?" "What is the difference between Jung and Freud?" "How much does it cost, and why does it cost so much?" "Why is there so much secrecy about it?" "Isn't it a passing fad?" "Why must you lie down?" "Doesn't it make you morbidly introspective?" "Do you ever get free from it?" "Does the patient always fall in love with his analyst?" "Isn't it dangerous?" "Does it ever do anybody any good?" "Why can't you be analyzed by a relative or friend?" "Who comes to analysis anyhow?" "Does it mean that you are crazy, if you have to be analyzed?"

In the following chapters many of these questions and others will be discussed in an effort to clear away some of the misconceptions which lie behind them. In doing so, it is our hope that anyone who is contemplating being analyzed will acquire a helpful foretaste of what the experience will be like, and at least an inkling of the difference between valid psychoanalytic procedures and practices which masquerade under its banner. Furthermore, it may help the prospective patient to complete his analysis successfully if his family, his friends, and his referring physician have some understanding of the nature of the voyage on which he is about to embark.

PRACTICAL AND THEORETICAL
ASPECTS OF PSYCHOANALYSIS

I. General Introduction

Chapter I

FREUDIAN PSYCHOANALYSIS

Psychoanalysis is a specific technique for studying and influencing the form, the distribution, and the utilization of psychological forces.

The Domain and the Technical Objectives of Psychoanalysis

A scientific method is comprehensible only when one understands what it attempts to do in relation to some natural phenomena. Although psychoanalysis is a complex instrument, its subject matter and its aims can be summarized simply: (1) In every man there are psychological processes of which he is unconscious, as well as those of which he is conscious. (2) At every moment of life the unconscious processes play an important contributory role in determining much of our behavior. (3) Where they play a dominant role, the resulting behavior cannot be influenced materially without first altering the underlying unconscious psychological processes. (4) In order to do this it is necessary to find out what they are. (5) This requires the use of special techniques, among which the pioneer and still the most important is psychoanalysis. (6) The purpose of this technique is to overcome the internal obstacles which interfere with the emergence of unconscious processes into consciousness. (7) At the same time the technique aims to modify the disturbing and sometimes destructive influence of the unconscious processes as they are brought into consciousness. (8) Therefore, in therapy, in prevention, and in education, the inclusive goal of psychoanalysis is to broaden the domain of conscious control in human life, and to shrink that darker empire in which unconscious forces play a dominant role.

1

This summary embodies much controversial matter; but instead of entering into the pros and cons of these controversies, the summary itself will constitute the working hypothesis of this book.

Psychoanalysis then has as its goal the uncovering and the modifying of unconscious psychological forces. With a technique designed to achieve this purpose, psychoanalysis attempts to prevent and to relieve suffering whenever it is caused primarily by mental processes of which the patient is himself unaware. Psychoanalysis cannot be used to shield the patient from the accidents of life. Nor can it prevent diseases that are primarily organic in origin. In such situations the most it can do is to increase the patient's resistances to adversity and to disease by lessening the destructive influence of unconscious emotional stresses. Therapeutically its significance is proving greatest where the unconscious forces are most important; and by and large its value is most restricted where purely environmental forces or bodily changes play a primary role in the process of illness.

Psychoanalysis began as a treatment for the neuroses, and primarily for but one type of neurosis. Gradually it has extended its domain, sometimes successfully, sometimes with difficulties. Whenever a new medical technique is discovered some degree of over-expansion is inevitable for a time. Whether it be a technique of investigation or of treatment, it is tried out hopefully on every old and unsolved problem. Like Leuwenhoek with his microscrope, the psychoanalyst has been eager to examine every mental aberration which comes to hand.

The basic relationship of psychoanalysis to health in general will be more clearly understood when the modern concept of the neurotic process is described in Chapters II and III.

The Name

In medicine every specific method of treatment or of investigation needs its own descriptive name. A tumor may be treated by surgery, X-ray, radium, or by other means; and without specific names for each method, much confusion would result both in scientific writings and in popular understanding. The same holds true for the various techniques and theoretical systems within the general domain of psychiatry.

Certain of the early workers who deviated from Freudian psychoanalysis recognized the soundness of this principle, and coined special designations for their divergent methods: as, for instance, the "Analytical Psychology" of Jung, the "Individual Psychology" of Adler, or the "Phyloanalysis" of Burrows. Some more recent innovators prefer to think of themselves, and with some reason, not as anti-Freudian but as neo-Freudian; and for their varied degrees of divergence in theory or technique they continue to use the term "psychoanalysis." Just where to draw the line is difficult to say. Certainly, it would not be wise to be arbitrarily dogmatic. The general principle is clear, but its application is far from easy. Thus it is in everyone's interest so to limit the term that it will characterize for laymen and for physicians alike a certain set of basic hypotheses and a related method for dealing with psychiatric and psychological problems. This enables everyone to understand what the term means; and it makes it possible accurately to compare the relative efficacy of different methods.

At the same time, the term must be used broadly enough to make room for those changes and developments which come with experience and technical experimentation. Otherwise there is danger of stagnation. How the present organization of psychoanalysis tries to avoid this danger will be explained below.

Dictum of the British Medical Association

In 1929 after a careful investigation by an impartial committee, the British Medical Association formulated the following definition and rules concerning the use of the term "psychoanalysis." In certain respects the situation has changed since 1929, but the general principle laid down at that time still merits consideration. (*British Medical Journal*, Supplement, Appendix 2, June 29, 1929, p. 266, paragraphs 27 and 28).

"There is in the medical and general public the tendency to use the term 'psychoanalysis' in a very loose and wide sense. This term can legitimately be applied only to the method evolved by Freud and to the theories derived from the use of this method. A psychoanalyst is therefore a person who uses Freud's technique, and anyone who does not use this technique should not, whatever other method he may employ, be called a psychoanalyst. In accordance with this definition and for the purpose of avoiding confusion, the term 'psychoanalyst' is properly reserved for members of the International Psychoanalytic Association. . . .

"Much confusion and misunderstanding relative to psychoanalysis has arisen from a failure to recognize and adopt the definition herein indicated. Thus, clearly, criticisms of psychoanalytical theory or practice should be confined to the teaching and methods of those who are psychoanalysts in the true sense of this term. This is not always so, and the Committee has received a number of reports and statements adverse to psychoanalysis as a form of medical treatment which on inquiry are found to be based upon methods put into operation not by psychoanalysts, but by other practitioners who adopt or accept the name but lack the qualifications."

The Present Status

This statement did much to clear away the confusion and misunderstanding then current; and as the demand for psychoanalytic treatment grew rapidly, it helped to check the exploitation of human need by men who pretended to be psychoanalysts but who lacked analytic training. The year 1929, however, was a period of transition. There were not enough Institutes to meet the demand for training. The Institutes which existed at that time were young and small and had not developed much individual prestige. Consequently the only authoritative source of sanction was the International Psychoanalytic Association.

To look upon any scientific body, however wise, as a sole or final arbiter on any scientific issue creates the danger of premature standardization and excessive rigidity. Consequently during the late '30s, psychoanalysts began to decentralize the authority of the International body. This process was hastened by the years of Nazi domination of the European continent and by World War II. Some of the continental psychoanalytic societies and Institutes were destroyed entirely; some were decimated by emigration and deaths; some went underground. By the end of the war the International Psychoanalytic Association consisted only of the Swiss, the British, and the Scandinavian societies, plus the societies which made up the American Psychoanalytic Association, some South American groups, one group in India and possibly one in Japan. In post-war Europe the old groups are forming again; and new by-laws for the International Psychoanalytic Association are being prepared. Under this new instrument the centralized control of training and of scientific issues which formerly was exercised by the International will be eliminated, and the sole function of the International will be to provide a forum for the exchange of scientific views and experience. All affiliated national societies or continental groupings of societies thus become arbiters of their own affairs. In this way an evolving diversification of theory and technique can develop within a framework of tried and proven principles, and a healthy emancipation is occurring in the practical definition of psychoanalysis and of psychoanalysts.

For the time being, however, in order to maintain high standards of training and to prevent the development of new confusions, it continues to be useful to define psychoanalysis as the professional activity of a group of men who have gone through a certain type of training. This in turn is acknowledged by their election to membership in local psychoanalytic societies, which are affiliated with and recognized by the national or continental association: e.g., the American Psychoanalytic Association for the United States and Canada. The decentralizing of authority described above makes it possible to use this as a practical working definition of psychoanalysis without serious danger of excessive rigidity and over-standardization. The popular notion as to who is a psychoanalyst will always be the truest index of the level of popular understanding of the essential scientific aspects of psychoanalytic theory and technique. This understanding will grow as a result of education both within the medical profession as a whole and among the laity. One of the purposes of a book such as this is to assist in that process of education.

Chapter II

WHAT CONSTITUTES AN ENLIGHTENED ATTITUDE TOWARDS PSYCHOLOGICAL AILMENTS

Until recently people thought that it was easy to be psychologically well, and that one was either wholly well or wholly sick. The "mind" was a unit, all of a piece. If anything at all was wrong with it, then you were either an eccentric or "crazy"; and in the latter case you should be put away in a special hospital. This would be necessary either because of the violence of your emotions or the "craziness" (i.e., the inaccuracy) of your ideas about the world. Gradually, however, the existence of a subtler but more frequent group of psychological disturbances was recognized. These came to be called the "psychoneuroses", or alternatively and for short, the "neuroses". For a long time the neuroses had been held in contempt. They were thought to be the result of some defect, which occurred only in unfortunate individuals who were somehow inferior to the rest. The word "neurotic" became a colloquial epithet, implying weakness or inferiority, except in certain paradoxical exceptions where the hypothetical inferiority seemed to have been transmuted into genius by some redeeming alchemy.

To some extent this attitude persists even among physicians. An internist who would not think of saying that a patient with typhoid was "typhoidic", or that a patient with a cold was "coldic", does not hesitate to speak of the patient with a neurosis as "neurotic", implying whether or not he realizes the implication, that there is something weak and inferior about this patient. Clearly there is no logic in this; yet to replace condescension by respect in the world's attitude towards patients with neuroses is proving to be a slow process. The popular assumption that more women have neuroses than men is another expression of this condescending atti-

7

tude. Actually, statistics from private and clinic practice prove that the reverse is true. People are coming slowly to realize that there is such a thing as a universal neurotic process which occurs in varying degrees in every living man, woman and child.

This admission comes slowly because man realizes that once he accepts the fact that the neurotic process is truly universal, he will have to face its manifestations and their consequences in his own life. And once he acknowledges this, he will have to do something about it. The admission comes slowly also because a special aura of guilt attaches itself to all psychological disturbances. In the mythology of the unconscious, mind-sickness is the ultimate punishment for sin. Therefore to admit that neuroses are universal is to admit that we are all sinners, and sinners in a secret and shameful sense. Thus there are powerful unconscious forces which obstruct the acceptance of the simple fact that the neurotic process is ubiquitous.

In the face of these obscurantist forces, the analyst must convince his fellow man that subtle and at times almost accidental factors determine whether this universal neurotic process will manifest itself in frank neurotic symptoms or in subtle personality traits. He must demonstrate that obvious neurotic symptoms may be so sharply circumscribed as to leave the rest of the personality not only unimpaired but often highly endowed both emotionally and intellectually, while the subtler manifestations of the neurotic process can escape recognition by hiding in the personality as a whole or in an entire way of life. The psychoanalyst hopes that ultimately the distinction between the "neurotic" and the "normal" will lose some of its misleading implications, as people come to realize that the one is a person with obvious symptoms and the other a similar individual who unwittingly has been able to conceal his symptoms in his personality.

In World War II, in every land and every culture wherever a statistically adequate cross-section of all young adult males was called up for military service, psychological disabilities were found to be more wide-spread than any other, regardless of geographic, national and cultural variations. In the United States these disabilities accounted for the rejection of one out of eight registrants for military service. Furthermore, despite the effort at preliminary screening, one third of the discharges from training camp were for similar disabilities. Among those discharged after combat, the psychological apparatus again proved to be the most frequent cause. Civilian experience demonstrates equally clearly that a subtle neurotic process is a universal component of human nature. Experienced internists point out that nearly 70 per cent of the patients who pass through their private offices suffer from psychological troubles. The same incidence is found in the out-patient departments and wards of general hospitals.*

From the top to the bottom of the economic and social ladder, in large urban centers, in isolated villages, on farms or in the woods, the same neurotic difficulties are found, and in approximately the same proportion. To illustrate, one sturdy family had served for many decades as fishing guides on a remote lake in Canada. One summer they found a psychiatrist among the guests; and before he left practically every member of two generations of that family had consulted him about neurotic symptoms which were indistinguishable from those which confronted him in his private office and in the out-patient clinic of a New York City hospital.

When we speak of psychological difficulties which are so widespread that no one escapes them, obviously we cannot mean illnesses which involve so profound a disorganization of the personality that the patient cannot take care of himself, so that for his own good and for that of his family and the community he has to be cared for in a special hospital. Such

* "The Organization of a Psychiatric Service for a General Hospital", *Psychosomatic Medicine*, vol. IV, No. 3, July 1942, pp. 252–272; and "The Impact of Modern Psychiatry on Medical Education, Medical Practice and Hospital Organization", *Bulletin The Johns Hopkins Hospital*, vol. 80, No. 6, pp. 348–360, June 1947.

patients are numerous enough; 630,000 beds in U.S. mental hospitals, and at least 415,000 more needed. But of the sufferers from the psychological ailments which we have been describing, the vast majority will never become sick enough to require hospital protection. It is safe to say that since every human being has some manifestations of the neurotic process, every psychotic patient in a mental hospital has also had a neurosis. Furthermore, it is probable that in many of these cases early treatment of the neurosis might have averted the ultimate total breakdown. This does not mean, however, that every neurotic, if untreated, is headed for a similar disaster.

Statistical samples indicate that in this country alone there are several million people who carry on their lives in the face of a daily struggle with troublesome psychological symptoms, which hamper them without wholly incapacitating them: such as bouts of seemingly causeless depression, sudden spurts of terror or anger, rigid obligatory rituals of thought or action (i.e., compulsive counting or compulsive handwashing), phobias which impose painful restrictions on their freedom (such as a terror of certain animals or of dirt, or an inability to go out in the street, or more than a certain distance from home, or higher than the lower floors of any building), or uncomfortable physical symptoms, with or without disturbances of bodily functions, for which there is no physical cause. These are only a few of the more obvious of the wide variety of symptoms of the frank neuroses. They are found in almost a tenth of the adult population, and in early childhood they occur universally as transient episodes; yet they constitute the smaller part of the total problem.

Only exceptionally does the neurotic process occur as the result of some startling or unusual occurrence or some melodramatic life situation. The rule is rather that it results from the everyday stresses of family living. Consequently the neurotic process is found in all economic, intellectual and cultural strata, in the city and in the country, in highly civilized centers and on the frontiers of civilization. Until we shall have learned a great deal more about these universal emotional stresses of human life, neuroses will continue to arise everywhere. A gradual recognition of this fact is making us humbler and more tolerant towards all manifestations of the neurotic process. From the study of individual patients we can hope in time to learn how to prevent much of the neurotic suffering which attends human life today.

The ultimate prevention of the neurotic process can bring humanity to its first true maturity. We are emerging from an era of human history which spans all recorded time, an era in which it has been assumed naively that it is easy to be psychologically well. Slowly we have learned that this is not so, and that to be a human being is so complex a task that the human race is not yet up to it. We have learned that wisdom about the world around us, scholarly erudition, high purpose and even religious faith have not alone or together been able to prevent neurotic distortions of human life. We must also admit humbly that we still know so little about the processes of normal development that the adult who is truly normal is still a happy accident.

There is no valid evidence, however, that man has become more neurotic. It is clear that in this age of increased life expectancy, growing population density and unlimited destructive power, we can no longer tolerate the destructive influences of unconscious psychological forces which the world once could accept with relative impunity. This is why the solution of the problem of the ubiquitous neurotic component of normal human nature is so pressing. Its solution affects the welfare of all, but can be found only through the study of the individual. Therefore, every time that analysis helps one human being to rid himself of his neurotic difficulties by tracing his neurosis to its roots, all of us have gained a fragment of knowledge that may help to save the world. And every individual patient who subjects himself to analysis is making a contribution not to his own happiness alone, but to the general good as well.

Chapter III

THE CONCEPT OF NORMALITY AND THE
NEUROTIC PROCESS

Psychoanalysis is uncompromising in its concept of mental health. The analyst is not content with a statistical definition of normality as being that which "most people" do or feel or think. Common colds are illnesses, even though everyone catches colds; and dental caries is not "normal" merely because most of us have cavities in our teeth. The physiologist does not think that he has explained the subtle mechanism of the heart-beat by stating that everybody's heart beats. No more does the psychoanalyst feel that the mere fact that most people behave in a certain way makes it superfluous to seek the reason *why* they do so. The answer that "everybody does it" may be a statement of a fact, but is never its explanation.

Nor is the analyst content to use conformity to the cultural mores of any time and place as his criterion of normality. It will be shown below that neither conformity nor rebellion is necessarily or intrinsically normal. Neither do the usual medico-legal distinctions between the sane and the insane throw light on the essential contrast between normality and illness. These legal definitions deal only with the practical distinction between those people who for the good of the community should be held responsible for their conduct, and those who for any one of several reasons must be safeguarded, like children, from the consequences of their own impulses. Whether or not a man "knows the difference between right and wrong" in the archaic and unreal legalistic sense, or whether or not he believes that he knows both *what* he is doing and *why* he is doing it, is of limited significance. Many insane people know the difference between right and wrong quite as clearly as a clergyman; and many who think that they can fully explain their own conduct are merely deceived by pseudo-rational explanations. Nor does the difference

12

between normal and neurotic conduct depend upon the degree
to which an act contributes either to the welfare of society
or to its destruction, or on whether the behavior is extravagant
and fantastic or orderly and sedate.   Certainly from the
point of view of society all of these are important attributes
of human behavior; but they are neither constant nor explana-
tory as a basis for the distinction between the normal and the
neurotic process.   Thus in the mere act of handwashing there
is nothing eccentric or anti-social or deviant from any culture;
yet it is not normal to wash one's hands thousands of times per
day.   This is not because the act itself becomes different when
it is repeated, but because there is a fundamental difference
in the purposes which the act serves.   Similarly, to stand
on your head in a tumbling act is normal, while to stand on
your head in church is not, unless perhaps it is done to pay
an election bet or as a hazing stunt.   Evidently the critical
difference lies not in the act, nor in its setting, but in the
psychological mechanisms which determine the act.   It will
be shown that it is the nature of the inner forces which produce them, which determines whether personality and behavior are normal or neurotic.

The Role of Conscious and Unconscious Forces

Through psychoanalysis we have learned that every moment
of human life, and indeed everything that we do or think
or feel is determined not by one psychological process operating alone but by whole constellations of processes, and that we
are aware of some of these and wholly unconscious of others.
Starting from this basic fact, psychoanalysis has made it clear
that human behavior is normal precisely to the degree to
which it is determined by conscious processes, and neurotic
insofar as it is determined by unconscious processes.   This
holds true equally for individual acts and for personality
traits as a whole.*

* It may be that the normality and maturity of a culture or of an entire
civilization depends equally upon the extent to which conscious purposes
determine its customs.   This is a proposition for sociologists and cultural
anthropologists to examine.

At this point the reader might ask why it makes so much difference whether conscious or unconscious processes drive the engine and steer the car. It is because the processes of which we are conscious can be influenced by appeals to reason, by argument and exhortation, by success and failure, by rewards and punishments. Consequently, that part of the personality which is determined predominantly by conscious processes has the capacity to adapt flexibly to external realities and to learn from experience. To the extent, therefore, to which conscious processes govern our lives we are free, free to learn and to grow in wisdom and understanding. Such freedom, indeed, is the only psychological freedom which psychoanalysis recognizes; and it is the essential core of normality. In contrast to this, those thoughts, feelings, behavior and personality traits which are determined predominantly by unconscious psychological processes are for that very reason rigid and inflexible. Precisely because the determining forces are unconscious, they cannot be swayed by argument or reason, by exhortation or persuasion, by appeals to feelings or to loyalty, by rewards or punishments. Furthermore, since unconscious forces pursue the symbolic representations of unknown goals which they can never attain, those cravings which are determined by unconscious forces are insatiable; and the behavior which expressed such needs must repeat itself endlessly, repeating errors as frequently as successes, regardless of the happiness or unhappiness which it occasions. Consequently, to the extent to which behavior is driven by unconscious forces it can learn nothing from experience, and can never develop or change or grow. In the truest sense of the word, it is enslaved.*

That is why the relative role of conscious and unconscious psychological processes in human affairs is perhaps the most important single fact that can be determined about human personality, human behavior, and human institutions.

Neither conscious nor unconscious processes ever operate separately. A mixture is always at work; and the distinction

* Cf. "The Repetitive Core of the Neurosis", *Psychoanalytic Quarterly*, Vol. X, 1941, pp. 23–43.

between normality and neurosis is relative rather than absolute. The more preponderant is the influence of conscious forces, the more normal is the resulting behavior; and vice versa. It is a further corollary of this definition that there is no single human quality and no human act or thought or feeling which cannot be either normal or neurotic or both. Thus benevolence can certainly be both normal and valuable, but when it is compulsively over-driven by unconscious necessity, it can be destructive both to the giver and to those whom it attempts to serve, by defeating itself in the pursuit of unattainable unconscious goals. Similarly a high tolerance for pain, frustration, or uncertainty can be a most valuable human trait; but when it serves an unconscious need to suffer, the capacity to endure becomes a measure of illness and not of health. Similar reservations must be made about the human drive to work, to play, to eat, to fight—indeed, about anything that man can do. This brings us back again to our fundamental principle, namely that it is not what we do but why we do it which counts. Or to put it more explicitly, it is not in the quality or value to others of an act or trait but in the inner forces which determine it that we find the essential distinction between psychological sickness and psychological health.

This is far from being a purely theoretical distinction. Quite on the contrary, it has practical consequences from infancy to the end of life. Take as an example the disturbances of behavior which occur in the development of every child. Those which are determined by conscious processes can be corrected quickly and easily by simple common-sense devices: e.g., by distracting the child, by punishing him or rewarding him suitably, by argument, by affection, by sternness, by flexible modifications of the situation, and the like. When, on the contrary, the identical behavior is determined predominantly by unconscious forces, it will resist all such efforts, and can be modified only if and as changes occur in the unconscious forces which produce the behavior.

Thus our unconscious needs and our conflicts over our unconscious needs become the source of all that is obsessive, rigid, and compulsive in human behavior. They enslave reason and subject it to their own purposes; and when reality frustrates them, or when they are deadlocked within us they give rise to all of the familiar manifestations of anxiety, depression, confusion and anger which haunt men's lives. This implies that the neurotic in human nature causes all that is ridden with anxiety, driven by anger, paralyzed by depression, and lost in confusion. This occurs because our most important inner conflicts take place on levels to which our conscious self-perceptions cannot penetrate without outside aid.

Our consciously organized processes contrast sharply with this. Since they are conscious, the individual is able to consider them with clarity. He can gauge his chances of achieving his goals by one path or another. He can be experimental and adaptable in his efforts. He will appraise the difficulties realistically; and if they are too great, they will deter him from attempting the impossible or will spur him on in the legitimate hope of success in the end. In short, the man who is normal in this sense can accept the guidance of reason, reality, and common sense. The outside world may be unyielding; but he remains flexible, modifiable, and educable, and therefore, in a pragmatic sense, *free*. This indeed is the Fifth Freedom, the most important freedom of all, i.e., the freedom from the tyranny of the unconscious. It is the essence of the psychoanalytic concept of normality.

In this sense, even in the complete absence of outspoken neurotic symptoms, a man may be "neurotic" to the degree to which his life may consist of compromises with unconscious conflicts and unconscious purposes. By compensating for them as best he can, he may achieve some degree of mastery over them, without ever becoming free from their secret influence.

Over the years such compromises gradually work less and less well, until finally there is some kind of collapse, which is commonly called a "nervous breakdown". This may be nothing more than a period of depression or of pseudo-physical illness; or it may manifest itself in sudden and perhaps unwise changes in marriages, occupations or homes, or through some more serious mental disturbance. What Lincoln is supposed to have said of the public is equally true of that which goes on inside Everyman in his dealings with his own unconscious. We may be able to fool part of ourselves all of the time, and all of ourselves part of the time; but we are not able to fool all of ourselves all of the time. This is why we pay so high a price for the unresolved neurotic forces which lie hidden in all of us.

To the analyst therefore, normality means freedom from the masked as well as the overt neurotic tendencies of the personality. Freedom such as this is manifested in the strength to withstand the pressure of external events, in the ability to tolerate uncertainty without generating excessive anger on the one hand or paralyzing anxiety or depression on the other, and through the absence of blindly compulsive activity.

Much remains to be discovered about how these unconscious processes arise in infancy, how and why they split off from the stream of conscious events to initiate the neurotic process, and how this process may be checked or at least guided into less destructive channels.

(1) We know that for various reasons early in infancy painful psychological conflicts are subjected to a process which is called "repression", in the course of which all memory or awareness of them is pushed out of consciousness.

(2) We know, furthermore, that these buried conflicts do not thereupon become inert or inactive. Instead, forces which have their roots in the repressed conflicts become detached from them, to exercise a powerful although unrecognized influence upon our conscious processes. Consequently, behavior is always a product of conscious and unconscious processes acting jointly; and the latter are represented in disguised and symbolic forms in all of our actions, thoughts, and feelings.

(3) As a result, any human need, however legitimate it may be intrinsically, can be either compulsively over-driven

or anxiously denied and inhibited, whenever forces derived from unconscious processes acquire a dominant role over it. This is how a child's natural and healthy need for food can be distorted into a total refusal to eat or an insatiable need to eat to the point of vomiting. Any unconscious necessity, as long as it remains unconscious, can be gratified only symbolically, which means that in reality it is never gratified at all. These unconscious processes are the scars of the buried conflicts of infancy and childhood. Since they may remain with us throughout life, they are a source of the many insatiable and repetitive needs, fears, activities and habits which make up so much of human personality as we know it.

(4) The neurotic process is always a symbolic process: and the split into parallel yet interacting streams of conscious and unconscious processes starts approximately as the child begins to develop the rudiments of speech. This rudimentary speech is at first a language of action and not of words; but there is good reason to believe that the evolution of the capacity to use language is linked closely to the process by which we first repress and then represent our unconscious struggles. Consequently, throughout life everything we do and feel and think is both symbolic and realistic at the same time; and the extent to which any piece of behavior serves as a symbol for something else measures the degree to which it has been shaped by unconscious forces. It may be accurate to say, therefore, that the neurotic process is the price that we pay for our most precious human heritage, namely our ability to represent experience and communicate our thoughts by means of symbols, and through such symbols to discharge some at least of the psychic tensions which we bury in ourselves during our struggles with our instincts and our life experiences. Thus the highest potentialities of the human psyche and its susceptibility to neurotic distortion are closely related to each other; and all hope of any fundamental progress in human nature depends upon our learning how to preserve the creative potential which is inherent in the symbolic process, while limiting and controlling its potentialities for neurotic distortion.

The transient neurotic episodes which occur in every childhood are the first manifestations of this neurotic distortion of symbolic functions. Familiar examples are the nightmares, the commonplace facial twitchings and tics, the stereotyped behavior habits, the exaggerated loves and hates, the blind rebellion and equally blind submissiveness, the timidity, self-consciousness and shyness, the food phobias and eating compulsions, etc. These universal troubles of childhood are the larval manifestations of the process out of which adult neuroses evolve; and since at the present stage in the evolution of human nature these episodes are universal and are never wholly erased, some residue in adult years is also universal.

Therefore, what passes for normality in our world today is not in any fundamental sense normal. It is rather the unstable equilibrium between conscious and unconscious processes, by means of which men have hidden the unconscious mechanisms which infest their daily activities. The activities which result may not be peculiar or strange in themselves. They may be socially acceptable and even valuable; and they may meet all the demands of conscience. Yet they can, nonetheless, express the distorting influence of unconscious forces. Thus, the way we live, eat, work, make love and bring up our children, our attitudes towards politics, economics and international affairs, how we play, our choice of companions, how we dress and sleep, our attitudes towards pain and suffering (both our own and that of others), our tolerance for uncertainty, our proneness to anger or to depression, our tendencies towards dependence or independence, how we react to success and failure, our morals, the balance in us between generosity and selfishness —all of these and many other personality traits are consequences in the adult personality of the residues of the unresolved neurotic problems of childhood. These residues make us what we are as craftsmen, artists, professional men, citizens, husbands, wives, parents, and friends. They determine the peace of mind, serenity, and gaiety with which we are able to live, or the veiled tensions, anxieties and angers which discolor our lives. They can be the source, equally, of greatness of spirit or of meanness and crime; and they can cost us much of the happiness which would otherwise be ours for the taking. They lie at the heart of that oldest of human problems, human discontent. They are the veiled and universal neurotic component of "normal" human nature.

Some Additional Comments

The foregoing discussion of normality and the neurotic process is reasonably accurate, but not quite the whole story. There are three potentials in the make-up of every human being—a neurotic, a psychotic, and a creative potential. These three potentials are not only universal (except among the mentally defective) but relatively constant. Yet, out of them three enormously variable processes evolve slowly—a neurotic, a psychotic, and a creative process. Not only do these three processes interact continuously on one another; but they are also molded constantly by the concurrent influence of varied individual experiences, cultural pressures, and physiological differences. Consequently, the processes change progressively as they evolve. Some of the forces that determine the course of these three streams are intrinsic to the personality and arise out of our earliest life experiences; some are dependent upon the impact of physiological variables; others result from the varied social conditions under which people live. At critical junctures in life, states of illness may occur, precipitating either the clinical neurosis or the clinical psychosis; or states of free creative productivity may be reached. The full story of the complex, interwoven evolution of these three ingredients in human nature is the story of human life, of human creativity, and of human tragedy. It is into this complex stream that psychoanalysis attempts to introduce its influence.

(A more complete technical exploration of these problems can be found in the group of studies listed in the Bibliography for this chapter.)

Chapter IV

THE GENERAL NATURE OF NON–TECHNICAL
PSYCHOTHERAPY*

Psychotherapy existed long before there was a name for it. Indeed psychotherapy is as old as medicine and nearly as old as religion. Its story would be a history of human civilization. Yet only the last half-century has brought scientific knowledge of its scope and limitations; and it is only in the last half-century that anything new has been added to its techniques.

The term, though young, has already acquired too vague and general a meaning. It is used at times for the mystical healing rites of a priest-physician of ancient Greece, the drum-beating and the voodoo practices of a modern primitive, David strumming his lyre against Saul's melancholy, classes in rhythmic dancing in a modern psychiatric hospital, forced labor in an old prison asylum, the monotone of a class in basket weaving, lectures on ideals of healthy living, dramatizations of human conflicts, an assortment of modifications of hypnotism, or the most subtle and sophisticated psychoanalytic technique.

In this broad sense, psychotherapy includes every effort to shape human thought, feeling and behavior, whether by education, precept or example, by command or exhortation, by reason and logic, by humor or emotional inspiration, by distraction and diversion, by stern discipline or by indulgence and deliberate escapism, by punishments and rewards, by direct material relief or by gross or subtle alterations in the external environment. It can include the influence on the individual of such cultural forces as religion, music, the arts, and literature. These devices are by no means new; nor were

* Adapted, with the Editor's permission, from L. S. Kubie: "The Nature of Psychotherapy", *Bulletin of the N. Y. Academy of Medicine,* March, 1943, Vol. 19, No. 3, pp. 183–194.

they invented by psychiatry. They have always been resorted
to by parents, teachers, religious leaders, and social workers.
The Greeks in their healing temples used music and occupational therapy as adroitly as does the modern hospital; and
while these are most effective if applied with patience, tact,
intuitive sympathy, and practical wisdom, they require little
technical psychiatric knowledge. Nor are they the specific
tools by which the neurotic process as such can be altered,
much less cured; and no matter how imaginatively they are
used, they can never by themselves resolve the unconscious
conflicts which every adult inherits in some degree from his
own infancy and childhood.

It is our thesis that psychotherapy as a science begins where
these simple yet venerable methods leave off. Thus, it is
usually good sense to give water to a thirsty man; but this
is not science until we know the role of water both in the
normal body and in illness. So too, with all such simple
psychotherapeutic sips of water as sympathy or advice, or
rewards and punishments: we can use them with scientific
precision only when we know their relationship to normal and
disturbed functions of the mind, on both conscious and
unconscious levels. Thus, the term psychotherapy is used
in two senses: (1) as a name for all homely common-sense
aids to wise and peaceful living, i.e., non-technical psychotherapy; and (2) as a technical term for certain specific methods of altering the neurotic process, methods which take up
where the simpler remedies fail.

Obviously, psychotherapy * cannot always achieve or even
aim at the eradication of causes. As with any other medical

---

* The psychotherapies can be classified in various ways. It frequently is useful to group them
under three headings, like three partially overlapping bands in a continuous spectrum. (1) At
one end is simple non-technical, non-analytic psychotherapy, which deals primarily with conscious
situational problems and conflicts. Without considering unconscious conflicts, it offers instruction,
guidance, rewards and punishments, vocational training, material relief, distraction, encouragment,
and exhortation, and usually helps the patient to master or suppress troublesome conscious
problems and impulses. (2) In the next category or band is analytically informed psychotherapy,
which may be both palliative and in some measure expressive. Here the therapist is alert to the
interplay of unconscious forces in his patient's life, and takes them into consideration in dealing
with symptoms; but he makes no effort to impart this understanding to the patient. (3) Finally
comes analysis itself, the crux of which is the effort to share with the patient full insight into
unconscious mechanisms. This is done by interpreting to him his transference phenomena,
resistances, free associations, waking fantasies, dreams, and the patterns of his daily living, as
well as his frank neurotic symptoms. These analytic devices will be dealt with in subsequent
chapters. The simpler components of psychotherapy will be considered here.

therapy, it must sometimes content itself with palliative measures, in which the homely common-sense maneuvers may play a major role.

Non-technical Psychotherapy as a Practical Test of the Severity of a Disturbance

Non-technical psychotherapy performs several essential functions which fall naturally into three categories: (a) *Practical support*, consisting primarily of advice, guidance, and assistance through social service in the management of life situations and environmental difficulties, occupational guidance, etc. (b) *Emotional support*, consisting essentially of sympathy, exhortation, admonition, encouragement, humor, art, recreation, companionship, etc. (c) *Reorienting education*, consisting primarily of efforts to alter the patient's habitual conscious attitudes of guilt, fear, hate, and depression, by educating him to recognize and tolerate his own conscious needs and cravings, his instinctual hungers, and his familial jealousies and hates, etc.

Deliberately or inadvertently, this third group often penetrates to unconscious levels. When it does so, it requires some knowledge of the workings of unconscious psychological forces. Furthermore it harbors certain dangers which will be discussed below. The first two, however, are the homely non-specific weapons of every wise parent and teacher; and these must always be tried first. Indeed where they succeed alone, one may be sure that the maladjustment was external rather than internal; since it is precisely the failure of the simple therapeutic devices which demonstrates the presence of that rigidity which stamps behavior as neurotic, in the sense that it is shaped predominantly by unconscious forces, rather than by conscious forces or external stresses. This, again, is why psychotherapy as a technical science begins where the simpler methods fail.

A banal example may make this clear. A child of three or four wakens at night, slips out of his bed, and comes pattering into the front room in search of his parents. On the first occasion he is picked up, hugged, and carried back to bed; and after his wants are attended to he is tucked in, kissed, and left there. A few minutes later, however, he reappears. The same procedure is followed, perhaps a little more brusquely, but nonetheless kindly. Even if it did not work the first time it might work now. But again the youngster appears. The parents try successively leaving the light on, the door open, a toy in his bed, cuddling, promises, bribes, scoldings, threats and punishments; but in spite of their versatile efforts the child reappears over and over through the course of many evenings. The parents become distracted. They run through the whole gamut of feelings, from affectionate patience to irritability, anger, and finally a panicky feeling that something must be wrong, and a guilty conviction that they are failing in their responsibility as parents. They do not realize that their seeming failure was a necessary therapeutic test, which proved that the roots of the child's disturbed behavior were on a level which was inaccessible to surface manipulations. Actually, their handling of the situation demonstrated that they confronted one of the typical, transient, neurotic episodes of childhood.

Common-sense maneuvers thus constitute a practical test of the severity of any psychological upset. Where they succeed, their success proves that the roots of the disturbance are superficial. On the other hand, where after persistent use they fail, the failure proves that the disturbance is more deep-seated. This fact is self-evident, yet it often is overlooked. Patients, their families, and their physicians often blame themselves for the time which has been consumed in giving these simple preliminary measures an adequate trial. Such self-reproaches are justified only when we try to terrorize symptoms out of sight by excessive penalties, or to bribe them into silence by over-indulgence, or when, in spite of repeated failures, we persist too long with futile efforts. Such mistakes as these are most likely to occur either where no technical psychiatric help is available, or among those who harbor a blind prejudice against turning to psychiatry under any circumstances (cf. Ch. XIV).

What is true of the small child is equally true of the adult. Rewards and punishments, discipline and education, argument and reason, the sensible manipulation of the environment, occupational therapy, comfort, solace and exhortation, all these are helpful preliminary steps in the approach to any psychotherapeutic problem.   They clear away external complications.   They effect cures when the situation is sick rather than the individual.   They are at once an ante-chamber to deeper treatment, and a practical therapeutic test of its necessity.   Where they achieve lasting therapeutic results it is certainly folly to go deeper; but where they fail, it is even greater folly to persist, because, until the internal obstacles are eliminated, the neurotic patient cannot make effective use of such aids, no matter how badly he may need and crave them.   Indeed technical treatment of a true neurosis must usually precede or at least accompany practical non-technical assistance; otherwise even the wisest and most benevolent guidance will usually be sabotaged by the neurotic process.

Palliative Psychotherapy

Palliative psychotherapy consists primarily of an effort to teach patients how to live with some measure of comfort within the confines of their uncured neuroses.   By itself this can sometimes relieve much suffering.   For instance, what is called "agoraphobia" may at first manifest itself merely in an uneasy feeling when the patient is out in very large, open spaces.   At this stage the neurosis will make relatively little difference in his life.   Gradually, however, the anxiety will become more all-pervading, until finally the patient may be unable to go out of doors at all, or unable even to leave his own room lest he be confronted by the challenge of a room that may be even slightly larger than his own.   Thus his neurosis gradually imprisons him; and with each successive encroachment on his freedom, his life and that of his family become more circumscribed. Ultimately, all whose lives touch his in any way begin to pay with him the price of his illness. If through ingenious manipulations and his personal influence the psychotherapist achieves no more than to keep the patient from succumbing to these successive neurotic restrictions, if he merely keeps the prison walls from closing in, he will contribute greatly to the comfort and happiness of the patient and his family.

At the same time the palliative levels of psychotherapy often provide an invaluable foundation for ultimate curative treatment. By the time that a patient comes for help a severe neurosis may have caused such complete disorganization in his life that he can neither work, nor play, nor love, and thus is cut off from all sources of gratification and self-esteem. Intelligent preliminary psychotherapy and guidance may help such a patient to engage again in healthy, diversified activities, without which it might be impossible for him to undergo prolonged and intensive treatment.

Let me illustrate this with the problem of a man who came complaining of a severe height phobia. He was a doctor. Up to a point, his practice had expanded well as a result of a warm personality, and also because of his exceptional zeal and intellectual ability. Gradually, however, he had found himself increasingly crippled by the fact that he did not dare to go above the third or fourth floor in any building. If a colleague, or a patient, or a hospital ward or laboratory, or even a friend's apartment happened to be on a higher floor than this, he found himself in the grip of an attack of acute anxiety, sweating, his knees knocking together, short of breath, in fear of death, possessed by fantasies of throwing himself from the nearest window, unable to think or talk. The immediate effect of this upon his professional and social life was devastating.

But that was not all. The patient had suffered from these symptoms for several years before coming for help. As this futile struggle continued, he had acquired many tricks for fooling himself and others. He had learned a thousand dodges to avoid going up in high buildings, and to bring others down to him. On an auto trip, if anyone should happen to suggest a route which would take him over a high bridge, what had started out as a pleasure trip became a moral battlefield. Should he fight his terror and literally sweat it out; or succumb to it and insist on some alternate route, and then hate himself for his "cowardice"? He developed a tendency to exaggerate minor physical upsets or even to fake illness in order to dodge the anxiety-provoking situations. And with every evasion his self-hate and his despair increased, as well as his envy and rage against those who were not hampered as he was. Inevitably this bitterness had infected his relationship to his wife and children and to his professional associates; since those who were closest to him provided the most frequent occasions of his fears and were the witnesses of his retreats. Gradually the world became a finger pointed at him in derision. Although it was built on a simple neurotic disability, this complex superstructure of fantasies and feelings carried with it the threat of a major psychosis, and had worked at least as great an injury to the patient's life as had the original phobia.

Faced with this quite typical problem, palliative psychotherapy attempted first to remove the elaborate secondary structure, while at the same time attempting to show the patient less destructive ways of living within the confines of his neurosis, i.e., with a minimum of interference with his own life and that of his family. It taught him to handle his symptoms so as not to visit their consequences on his family and friends. It aimed to restore harmony and mutual tolerance and understanding both in his home and with his professional associates. Valuable as all of this was, however, it left unaltered the underlying neurotic conflict, which remained for analysis to remove, if the patient was ever to become well.

Such palliative help is of great human value as long as there are neurotic patients who cannot be cured completely, either because they live too far from anyone who is equipped to give deeper therapy, or because they are unable to devote sufficient time to treatment, or because of elements intrinsic to the neurosis itself, or because others in the family are opposed to intensive treatment in any form, or because they have postponed seeking treatment until it was too late for fundamental help.   Therefore, skillful palliative therapy should be highly valued; but it should be used only where for any of these reasons more fundamental treatment cannot be undertaken.

Dangers of Palliative Psychotherapy

In connection with these general introductory measures the psychotherapist must often undertake considerable emotional re-education.   As we have said, this consists of a cautious effort to increase a patient's tolerance for his own instinctual needs, for the bitter jealousies which are born in the nursery, and for the hostilities, fears and guilts which arise out of such conflicts.   In this aspect of treatment, group discussions are sometimes helpful and effective.

There are limits, however, to what can be achieved by any such direct educative procedures.   When they are pushed too far, patients will often reject those very truths about themselves which are most obvious to others.   Indeed, the more obvious the unwelcome truth, the more inevitable that the patient will be unable to accept it until the reasons for it and for his fear and guilt about it have been worked out with him. It is here that psychotherapy as a fumbling if benevolent art must give over to psychotherapy as a disciplined, scientific technique.

Indeed the most serious error to which every would-be psychotherapist is liable occurs in this connection.   We are constantly tempted to short-cut the tedious processes by which a patient's blind spots can be eliminated.   If we keep a critical watch on what we say and do, we will often find ourselves trying impatiently to cram insight down a patient's throat, like fattening a Strasbourg goose, forcing on him the guidance and instruction for which he is not ready. Many years ago William Alanson White said that the most difficult lesson a psychiatrist has to learn, and one which he has to relearn every day of his life, is to allow a patient to maintain that two and two is five, until the psychiatrist and the patient discover together why he has had to believe it. It is the discovery of the reasons for the patient's unconscious need tenaciously to cling to error, which alone makes lasting correction of the error possible. Consequently it often happens that as the result of months or even years of work, with great surprise and excitement a patient discovers facts about himself which have always been obvious to his friends and relatives. These then are likely to say, "Why, we knew that all along. We could have told you that! You didn't have to go to a psychiatrist to find that out." In saying this they indicate their failure to understand the essential principle of psychotherapy; namely, that "telling" the patient would have been useless until the therapeutic process had removed from the patient's mind the unconscious preconceptions and resistances, which for so long had made it impossible for him to recognize the obvious. Before these barriers are removed, no one can effectively tell a patient anything: once the inner barriers are gone, no one has to tell him.

This fundamental principle runs counter to a great deal of what is naively called common-sense; and since even experienced psychiatrists often violate this law of therapy, it is small wonder that physicians, nurses, laymen, clergymen, educators, and parents so frequently get into difficulties through their failure to appreciate its importance. They offer a patient excellent arguments, reassurances, consolation, or sound corrective advice, with all of which he may seem to agree eagerly. Then nothing happens, and the well-meaning advisers wonder why the patient failed to make wise use of their helpful counsel. Or, to their even greater dismay, the patient may react with panic or resentment or depression, instead of with the relief, reassurance and encouragement that his advisers had naively anticipated. This sort of disappointment is a daily experience for the psychotherapist who does not realize that the most critical step in therapy is the elimination of the internal obstacles to clear vision.

Nevertheless, it is worth while to reiterate that even such failures as these need not be without their value, provided only that the advice and confrontation has been offered gently, tentatively, and in small doses. The failures may become actually dangerous only when the adviser obstinately persists with his confrontations even after the patient has failed to profit by them. If, however, he realizes that the patient's recalcitrance arises out of resistances, the roots of which are unconscious, and if he modifies his approach so as to point the patient's attention to these resisting forces, then he will have helped his patient to take a long step towards the solution and cure of his neurotic difficulties.

There is one other lesson which every psychiatrist has to learn over and over again throughout his professional life, because he so often forgets it: namely, that however much it may relieve his own feelings, it does a patient no good to call his illness names. When a patient comes with a frank symptom, such as a handwashing compulsion, we know that it is a waste of breath to tell him solemnly that he suffers from a compulsion neurosis. In one way or another the patient tells us that himself. Our technical nomenclature can help him neither to control his symptom nor to get rid of it. Nevertheless, when dealing with subtler compulsive patterns this is often forgotten; and some psychiatrists hopefully describe to patients their "neurotic trends." There is no parent who has not told his child the same thing in laymen's terms, when he calls his child lazy or balky or ungrateful or disobedient. Pseudo-scientific name-calling is no more effective than parental name-calling as a way of altering the repetitive nucleus of any neurotic manifestation.

Thus it is impossible to over-emphasize the futility of naive confrontations, and their dangers when they are offered too insistently; because this is the most frequent mistake of the immature psychiatrist, and of the well-intentioned general practitioner who has read psychiatric theory without having been subjected to rigorous drill in procedure. Even superficial confrontations without careful preparation may precipitate resentment and mobilize defenses. Confrontations which reach to deeper levels, challenging the patient to recognize some of the buried sources of his difficulties, *must* be rejected by the patient if they are not to precipitate him into unmanageable terror, guilt or depression. One learns slowly not to force a patient to look at painful facts about himself until some understanding of their origins and purposes have been achieved. Sometimes, therefore, one may have to withhold interpretations during many months of patient exploration.

At times it may even be dangerous to attempt to argue a patient out of cherished ideas and beliefs about seemingly impersonal affairs, such as science, or politics. Occasionally, such an argument can be as dangerous as confrontation. If it succeeds too suddenly in breaking down the defensive barrier of symptomatic ideas, all that will result is an eruption of emotions before these can be digested. At times there may be similar danger even in reassurance and consolation. A patient said, "I was feeling all right until my sister happened to telephone me to tell me that her household was well. Then all of a sudden I found myself in such a panic and depression that I stood at the window and thought of throwing myself out." Thus, one slowly learns that the only wholly safe thing to do with a patient is to listen to him, until one understands enough about him to be in a position to relate one's comments to the patient's unconscious psychological processes.

"Mental Catharsis"

Most neurotic patients live in a state of constant inner tension of one kind or another. This gave rise to the notion that to discharge the pent-up feelings would work an automatic cure. Such a process of discharge is sometimes spoken of as mental "catharsis"; and from time to time much is made of it in psychiatric literature. It is important, therefore, to realize that catharsis alone is never enough. Furthermore, the concept is poorly understood and generally misused. Any discharge of emotional tension can give temporary relief, be it a temper tantrum or an uncontrolled outburst of crying and laughing. Indeed every neurotic symptom gives some momentary relief. A patient with a hand-washing compulsion discharges a certain amount of tension each time he washes his hands. In a broad sense, this is "catharsis", too. Unfortunately, however, until the source of tension is removed it re-accumulates rapidly.

It is cathartic in a somewhat more lasting sense, to enable a patient to express pent-up feelings which he has previously been unable to face. For instance, a man who has never been able to admit that he hated some member of his own family may feel marked relief when the psychiatrist's non-critical and permissive attitude enables him to acknowledge and express this feeling. Even here, however, unless a fresh upwelling of guilt or anxiety can be avoided, such a cathartic maneuver may precipitate the patient into subsequent depression and terror. Thus, no mere discharge of feelings, whether from the surface or from the depths, can accomplish lasting benefits unless it is preceded, or accompanied or followed by a gradual eradication of the unconscious sources of the feelings. Without this, the tension will recur inevitably.

The Role of Insight in Psychotherapy

In any organic disease, lasting therapy depends upon the elimination of the causal agents. This is equally true for those psychiatric illnesses which arise out of a system of unconscious conflicts and their derivatives. In order to dispose of these hidden trouble-makers, it is necessary first to bring them out into the full light of consciousness. Some of them thereupon prove not to be disturbing any longer because they were based upon childhood desires and misconceptions. Others can then be dealt with by conscious controls, without the production of disturbing symptoms. This is the generally accepted concept of the role of insight in the therapeutic process. Unfortunately, this most fundamental of all elements in psychoanalytic therapy has never been adequately tested and verified experimentally (v.i. Chapter XXV). Indeed, it is fair to say that this cornerstone of the modern conception of a dynamic psychotherapeutic process confronts us with many complex and unsolved problems. The word insight itself is applied to quite different levels of self-understanding. There is a superficially descriptive insight, which is merely the ability to describe honestly, and if necessary unsparingly, the way we have behaved. Even for those who can recall daily events with reasonable accuracy this is not simple. In keeping with the needs of our differing personalities, we usually color our memories, sometimes flatteringly, sometimes unfavorably to ourselves. Furthermore, our ability to appraise our daily experiences depends upon our ability to recall them. This is a variable faculty which is taken for granted when we have it, but which seems wholly unattainable when we lack it. There are some individuals who go through their days as though they were traversing a long corridor of doors, each of which they shut firmly behind them as they go, literally obliterating from their minds every detail of the day's journey, ending the day blank, but for a state of diffuse, unattached and unexplained emotion. At the other pole are those who can give a play-by-play account of every moment of the day, with an automatic and amazing facility for total recall of everything anyone said and did and felt. Most of us come between these two extremes. There are significant reasons for these marked differences, reasons which have to do partly with variations in the structure of the nervous system, but chiefly with variations in human nature. The capacity for spontaneous recall influences markedly our accessibility to therapy because the exploration of links with the past must start from current events. Since the present is a screen on which the past throws its shadows, we must study the present to find clues to the past; and the habitual obliteration of daily material blocks the exploratory process at its inception.

Experience, however, consists not of events alone, but also of feelings; hence, factual memory and factual recall is, by itself, only one component in insight. Here again there are marked variations in people. Some recall only feelings and no events; others only events and never their feelings. Some recall only what others did, and some only what they themselves have done. Again most of us fall between the extremes; but our position on the spectrum makes a difference in the ease with which we can acquire inclusive insight.

Finally, we find that for some people memory has only a short and recent span, whereas for others it tends automatically to go far back into early years. Memory is always full of gaps, however; and the first step in insight therapy is the effort to fill these in, whether they are in the recollection of recent or of remote experiences. Insight begins to have a therapeutic effect only when it leads to an appreciation of the relationship between buried experiences and the unconscious conflicts out of which arise both the neurotic components of the personality and the neurotic symptoms themselves.

Let us take as an example a young sailor who had gone through overwhelming stresses in battle in the Pacific, during the last war. After a particularly trying experience on a landing craft, he broke down with violent gastro-intestinal difficulties. When he came for treatment he had only one complaint, namely, a persistent diarrhoea; he recalled much of the details of combat; but he saw no connection between the two. The first goal of therapy was to give him an understanding of this connection: i.e., to enable him to feel vividly the relationship between the emotional strains through which he had passed and the persistent physiological disturbance.

His own associations to this material soon revealed another area of his life into which he lacked insight. This concerned the relationship between battle stress and certain painful situations of his early life. He had been raised in a home that had, in fact, been a living nightmare. He had been beaten and kicked and painfully mauled by older brothers and two young uncles, and had reacted to this treatment with incessant rage and terror. This was when his diarrhoea had started. He remembered a fair amount of this; but again he felt no connection between this and what he had gone through in battle. He did not realize that the gastro-intestinal disturbance which was precipitated in battle was a facsimile of a prolonged intestinal disturbance from which he had suffered in childhood, and that the battle stress was itself a re-experiencing of the misery of his earliest years. This was a second step in the acquisition of insight. Typically, insight must be acquired in just such a series of steps, which consist of the recapturing of the memory of events, and of emotional reactions to disturbing events, until finally an understanding of the relationship between old and recent pain, and between pain and symptom, is attained. This frequently means going back through one level of investigation after another. (Controversial aspects of this are discussed in Chapter XXV.)

It will become apparent at once, however, that in this discussion we have left far behind the narrow limitations of non-technical psychotherapy. The first step in the acquisition of insight (i.e., the correlation of a present symptom to an immediate strain) may be quite simple, and may require no specialized technical skill. Deeply rooted neurotic symptoms or traits, however, are rarely relieved by this maneuver alone. Usually, they must be traced to their roots in earlier experiences which have sensitized the patient to his current problems. This requires facility in the specific techniques of analytical psychotherapy. And it is to these that we will turn our attention in the succeeding chapters.

II. The How and Why of Psychoanalysis

Chapter V

THE EXPERIENCE OF BEING PSYCHOANALYZED

In the anticipatory fantasies of a prospective patient, psychoanalysis is neither a system of theories, nor a technique of treatment. It is an experience through which he is about to pass. Therefore it is natural that he should want to have some idea of what this experience is going to be like. A detailed preview is neither possible nor desirable; and only those will demand it who are over-anxious about the undertaking. Much of this anxiety has its origins in unconscious problems, and cannot be put at rest by descriptions of the process of analysis, however reasonable or reassuring. Therefore this chapter cannot hope to resolve the blind terror with which some patients approach analysis, but only to allay the more reasonable misgivings of the rest.

However, some anxiety is based on misconceptions, which persist in the minds even of supposedly educated people; such as the notion that most patients are wealthy women who have nothing else to do, and who come to analysis out of furtive, erotic curiosity; that the analyst asks the patient a great many embarrassing and exciting questions; that the patient, in the popular sense of the word, "falls in love with" the psychoanalyst; and that an analysis is conducted in an atmosphere of self-indulgent emotionalism. Some patients hope to carry away at the end a pearl of analytical wisdom, in the form of a written or oral digest of all their problems, together with an outline of guiding principles and directions as to what they should or should not do in the future. It is rare, nowadays, to find anyone who could not correct one or more of these misconceptions. In the minds of most laymen, however, and even of some physicians, fragments of these fantasies persist.

The realities of psychoanalysis are quite different. Patients usually approach analysis with hesitation and misgivings, under the pressure of their own wretchedness, or because of the urging of family, friends, or physician. Throughout the analysis they encounter an atmosphere of friendly courtesy, and quiet formality and reserve. They find that the psychoanalyst's private life, his tastes, his opinions and his personality are exhibited as little as possible, and that outside of the analytic session social contacts with the psychoanalyst are avoided. Indeed, if the psychoanalyst whom they first consult has had a prior relationship as friend or adviser, they discover to their surprise that he will usually send them to some other analyst who is a total stranger.

Once launched in the work of the analytic session, they find that instead of an affectionate and comforting friendship, they do not even hold ordinary conversations with the analyst. Usually they will lie on a couch with the analyst seated behind them; so that he is able to observe them without being under scrutiny himself. Therefore, they cannot watch his expression or respond to his apparent approval or disapproval; and when they try to laugh or joke with him about their troubles in an attempt to smooth them over, they find him bafflingly silent and unresponsive. They may talk for long periods with scarcely an interruption; while at other times they will be checked by insistent comments, comments which sometimes will make them more comfortable, but which, quite as often, prove to be disturbing.

Furthermore, the analysis makes formidable demands. It usually requires at least five sessions each week. Each session starts and stops punctually, and lasts as precisely as is possible for the period of fifty minutes which usually is agreed upon ahead of time. Patients are not encouraged to miss sessions for other obligations, whether pleasant or unpleasant, except when this is clearly unavoidable. They learn that they will usually be charged for scheduled sessions which they miss unnecessarily, and discover that it is difficult even to change the hour of an appointment. In short, the analysis turns out to be an exacting taskmaster.

As the analysis progresses, sooner or later the patient encounters periods of emotional turmoil and distress, intervals of peaceful satisfaction, moments of excited eagerness and hope, or arid weeks in which he cannot see where he is going or what progress he is making, and phases of anger, affection, friendliness, coolness, interest, impatience, boredom, resentment, skepticism, and a host of other unpleasant feelings.

The hypothetical patient who comes to analysis solely out of morbid curiosity or because he anticipates erotic titillation, soon finds his shallow motivation frustrated and exposed. His interest wanes, and he does not long continue to waste his own time or the analyst's before dropping out of the picture. On the other hand, the sincere patient somehow manages to carry on despite the pain, the time, and the expense, on the arid plateaux as well as over the mountain tops, through one or more years of intensive work.

At this point many questions arise about these grim features of the analytic process: why it takes so long, whether there are no shortcuts, why it goes on day after day for all that time, how one can find things to talk about for so long a period, and in the end what one gains from it all. We hope to answer all of these questions in the succeeding chapters.

Chapter VI

THE DURATION OF ANALYSIS AND THE FREQUENCY OF THE SESSIONS

The Duration of Psychoanalytic Treatment

The ills which are subjected to psychoanalytic treatment are never acute or passing ailments. For the most part they are chronic illnesses with occasional periods of acute exacerbation. The quiescent chronic phases of neurotic illness may often be mistaken for normality, just as the sufferer from tuberculosis may seem to be normal in the intervals between attacks, or for years before his infection first manifests itself openly. As Glover pointed out, there are illuminating analogies between the problems of treatment in the two illnesses. In each, the acute episodes may be of short duration; but the physician who is willing to discharge a patient as cured immediately after such an episode is either incompetent or unscrupulous. It is only when a sufferer from tuberculosis has become temporarily symptom-free that the long march towards enduring health begins. The same principle is valid in the treatment of neuroses. It is unreasonable to think that life-long illnesses, be they low-grade chronic infections or masked neurotic traits, can be cured in a short time. In both, one measures the duration of adequate treatment in terms of years and not of months. That psychoanalyst does his patient no service who fails to explain this to his patient before beginning the treatment, or who at the end of a few months of apparently successful analytic work interrupts the treatment without making it clear that the job is only partly done.

Many short methods have been sought, but none has yet been found. It may be that it is in the nature of these illnesses that none will be found, although any such pessimism is unjustified. The techniques of emergency treatment which were developed during the war have instigated many new investigations, some of which may bear fruit in the coming years.

These investigations are experimenting with various types of hypnotic phenomena in combination with analysis, with and without the use of various drugs. All of these methods aim at the induction of states of controlled dream-like dissociation, in an effort to facilitate the re-living of painful and forgotten experiences and the clarification of the multiple meanings of obscure symptoms.*

When he hears enthusiastic claims for new and rapid methods of treatment, the layman should bear in mind the fact that no other kind of research is as full of pitfalls as is research in therapy. In no other field are we equally vulnerable to the fallacies of wishful thinking. To offer a sick man a swift road to health is to offer him something for which he yearns. The conscientious psychoanalyst who warns prospective patients of the probable duration of treatment frightens many away. The temptation is great, therefore, to raise false hopes of rapid help. Unfortunately results have not yet justified these hopes.

One group of workers at the Chicago Psychoanalytic Institute has published papers and a book on what they have called

* Anyone who is interested in a more detailed discussion of the theory underlying these investigations and their results, and in the literature on this problem should consult the following publications:

Kubie, L. S., and Margolin, S.: "The Process of Hypnotism and the Nature of the Hypnotic State", *American Journal of Psychiatry*, Vol. 100, No. 5, March 1944, pp. 611–622.

Kubie, L. S., and Margolin, S.: "The Therapeutic Role of Drugs in the Process of Repression, Dissociation and Synthesis", *Psychosomatic Medicine*, Vol. VII, No. 3, May 1945, pp. 147–151.

Kubie, L. S.: "The Value of Induced Dissociated States in the Therapeutic Process", *Proceedings of the Royal Society of Medicine*, (London), Vol. XXXVIII, No. 12, October 1945, pp. 681–683 (Sec. of Psych. pp. 31–33).

Brenman, M., and Gil, M.: *Hypnotherapy*, Menninger Foundation Monograph Series 5, New York, International Universities Press, 1947.

"Psychoanalytic Therapy." In these they advocate experiments with an interrupted schedule consisting of a few weeks at a time of psychoanalytic work, interspersed with periods without treatment. They believe that this, together with certain other technical modifications, can materially shorten the time required for treatment, without sacrificing either the durability or the degree of the therapeutic achievement. It is entirely premature to attempt to pass judgment on these efforts. Some analysts claim that this is an important and promising new departure. Others maintain that this is merely what every psychoanalyst has been doing for years with the many patients for whom he did not believe that analysis was appropriate, or necessary or possible, either for psychological or for practical reasons. Neither of these conflicting claims has been adequately substantiated as yet, however, and a final judgment on them should be deferred.

The Frequency of the Sessions

The practice of psychoanalysis has evolved out of the experience of many mistakes, and each technical detail plays a part in avoiding their repetition. There is a reason, therefore, for the sacrifices which the analysis requires. Of these sacrifices none is more irksome than the daily session.

As the therapeutic work of the analysis proceeds, the incessant fluctuations of mood and tensions are observed and correlated with the impact of daily events. As this goes on, "forgotten" patterns of unhappiness are gradually brought to light: old fears, sorrows, guilts, angers, losses, conflicts, and frustrations. These come up for discussion in each day's work until their relationship to the external events in the daily life of the patient and to his psychological reactions becomes clear, and until he comes to understand how his own buried past can distort his daily attitudes and his ability to deal effectively and realistically with his current problems. The present is thus shown to be a screen on which the past constantly throws its shadows. To demonstrate these subtle correlations requires a continuous searching, backwards and forwards, between the past and the present.

Consequently the psychoanalyst keeps an attentive eye on the minute details of the patient's current life. Any interruption in the information which he receives about the stream of daily life temporarily deprives the psychoanalyst of that contact with current events, without which the dynamic significance of the past may be lost. Even weekend interruptions sometimes check the momentum of the work. Therefore, throughout the major portion of most analyses, the daily session proves valuable. A schedule of two or three analytical sessions a week tends almost inevitably to slow up the pace of the analytic process, and in some cases will stall the analysis completely. Nevertheless, in certain centers, psychoanalysts are trying to determine if and when it may be possible to do equally effective analytic work with a less continuous schedule, and with what types of illness, and with what changes in technique. That this can be achieved in certain cases has long been known, but the limits of the effectiveness of a discontinuous schedule are not yet clear.

There are many reasons why physicians and patients are tempted to diminish the frequency of the analytic sessions. For the patient it means a lessened strain upon his time and pocketbook. Furthermore, it seems to him that a day of freedom between analytic sessions gives him a breathing spell in which to carry on his usual life without interruption. Certainly these are practical advantages; but the loss of continuity in the work may prove to be too high a price to pay. Furthermore, the prized day of "rest" may become a day in which the patient withdraws from the analysis, both intellectually and emotionally; and to a degree this may jeopardize his progress.

Because it is popularly believed that long drawn-out treatments and daily sessions are financially advantageous to the analyst, it is worthwhile to point out that, on the contrary, precisely these features of analysis place a ceiling on the analyst's income. Indeed, from the analyst's point of view, every consideration of self-interest would tempt the busy practitioner to reduce the frequency of the analytic sessions. Were he to give each individual patient fewer appointments per week, each patient would be able to pay more per session. Furthermore, fewer sessions per patient would enable the psychoanalyst to take care of more individual patients at one time, with the result that the loss of one patient would make less difference in his income. For an analyst as for any doctor, the more patients he has at any one time, the more secure is his income. He can earn more and his earnings will be more secure if he takes care of more patients, for short treatments, and with less frequent sessions. The dismaying prospect of long months of daily work frightens off many potential patients; and the psychoanalyst who refuses to compromise in these matters has to content himself with a relatively modest and sharply fluctuating income. Nevertheless it is a fundamental principle of analytic practice to determine the frequency of the sessions not according to the patient's pocket-book but by the technical requirements of his neurosis. Thus, although it is both legitimate and essential to make experiments in varying the frequency of the sessions, if any analyst ventures to proclaim that "most patients do not need to come so often", he must be very careful that he is not using this statement as a rationalization of his own financial self-interest. We should study with interest and an open mind the therapeutic results achieved in recent experiments with less frequent sessions. But at the same time they should be scrutinized with cautious skepticism.

Chapter VII

THE TECHNIQUE OF FREE ASSOCIATION

In psychoanalysis the daily search for unconscious material is conducted by means of a method which is called "free association." In the development of psychoanalysis a series of experiments with other methods led to an increasing dependence upon free association as the technique without which it proved to be impossible to penetrate to unconscious levels of psychological activity.

Physiological Basis

The method of free association is in essence an application of the obvious fact that it is impossible for psychological processes to move from one thought to another unless there is a connection between them; just as it is impossible for a train to move from one station to another without a connecting track. The old saying that "one thought leads to another" is a popular statement of the same fact. We now know, however, that many associative links are unconscious; and it is the function of the psychoanalyst to discover the nature and meaning of unconscious as well as conscious linkages. He does this by studying the patient's free association.

Therefore the psychoanalyst notes not merely the conscious logic of a patient's communications, but also the sequence in time of his ideas and feelings. In his work on the conditioned reflex, Pavlov showed that in a hungry animal no two experiences could impinge upon the nervous system without setting up a connecting link, and that the nature of this link was dependent in part upon the time interval between them. Similarly in psychoanalysis it has been possible to prove that ideas, feelings and actions which occur together are bound to one another in a meaningful pattern. The nature

44

of that bond and of the inarticulate ideas which underlie it is often hard to ascertain; and much of the work of psychoanalysis is devoted to the investigation and translation of these bonds into conscious thoughts and feelings.*

Thus it has been the contribution of a great Russian school of neurophysiology to prove that time-relationships have a vital significance in psychophysiology; and it has been the contribution of the psychoanalytical school to make use of this fundamental principle in the study of unconscious psychological processes of thought and feeling.

Its Application

In applying this principle, the psychoanalyst asks the patient to make use of the simplest and most primitive of all ways of thinking: i.e., to allow his thoughts to flow without guidance or direction, bumping along from one idea to the next as a blindfolded man would bump from tree to tree in a forest. The patient is instructed never to withhold anything, never to substitute one thought for another because the other seems more relevant, never to omit anything because it seems impolite or unfriendly, a violation of confidence, embarrassing, or trivial and unimportant. In short, he is instructed to tell everything that passes through his mind, and, as nearly as this is humanly possible, to tell it in the order and in the form in which it comes to him. Thus, he is asked to think aloud in the presence of the psychoanalyst with that simple and naive form of undirected musing which everyone uses in the solitude of his own chambers, and which is at the same time the most spontaneous and creative of all forms of thought.

It is not always realized that free association is the natural process by which the mind of the artist and scientist creates. Free associations enable the psychological processes to roam

* Those who are interested in pursuing further this rather technical point may refer to an article in the *Archives of Neurology and Psychiatry*, Vol. 32, Dec. 1934, entitled "Relation of the Conditioned Reflex to Psychoanalytic Technic", and to two reviews of recent books on Pavlov from the psychoanalytic viewpoint. These will be found in the *Psychoanalytic Quarterly*, Vol. X, 1941, p. 329 and Vol. XI, 1942, p. 565.

through the mental highways and byways, unhampered by conscious restrictions, gathering up ideas and impressions, putting them together in varying combinations, until new relationships and new patterns come into view.   Both in science and in the arts, free association is an essential tool in the process of creative search.   Subsequent logical scrutiny subjects the new patterns to a necessary secondary process of retrospective checking and testing.   In analysis the free associations are provided by the patient, the logical scrutiny by the analyst.

It is important to realize that this dependence upon free associations is the basis of all that is new and scientific in psychoanalytic technique.   Ordinary conversational speech, logical and chronological thinking, the asking and answering of questions, arguments and expositions, are the product of a continuous automatic screening of the psychological process.   This screening selects certain ideas for attention because of their logical and chronological relationships, rejecting others as irrelevant.   On this depends our ability to organize thoughts and to communicate them.   The product of this selective process, however, is what the statisticians would call a weighted sample of our psychological processes, and consequently is not truly representative of all that goes on.   Free associations, on the other hand, may approximate a random sample of our psychological processes.   It is this special virtue of the technique of free association as a method of truer sampling, which makes it more valuable than any previous method of studying human personality and human psychology.

There are two psychological levels of linkages, one conscious and the other unconscious.   If we allow ourselves consciously to pick and choose from among the thoughts which come freely to mind, it becomes impossible to study the influence of unconscious forces on the stream of psychological events.   If, on the other hand, all conscious choices are eliminated, then the unconscious influences come into view.   Free associations, therefore, are the key to the unconscious, indeed the only key we now possess.

When the patient allows his thoughts to roam freely he gathers together a surprising array of apparently unrelated items. The well-trodden highways of his mind are soon abandoned and he finds himself in a seemingly trackless forest, following paths from which he can emerge only slowly. Sometimes it is possible to see almost at once the direction of the patient's thought processes; but more often the analyst's task is slowly to piece together a picture puzzle. Each day's work brings its additional bits of data, and only as the fragments of the puzzle accumulate over weeks and months can the pattern of the whole be made clear. Therefore both for the patient and for the psychoanalyst there are periods of searching, during which no rewarding answers and no immediate emotional gratification or relief from symptoms can be expected. However, as long as free associations continue to come from the patient without hindrance, the analysis progresses.

This would seem to be a simple requirement. Yet in the course of every analysis, free associations repeatedly become entangled in an intricate network of conscious and unconscious emotions, the resolution of which is one of the important therapeutic experiences of the analytic process.

The Value of the Struggle to Produce Free Association

"Why does just lying down and talking do anyone any good?"

When he attempts to produce a flow of free associations, to his dismay the patient finds this to be an unexpectedly baffling task. This most spontaneous of all forms of thinking, which in solitude is also the easiest, proves in the analytical situation to be the most difficult. From moment to moment the patient struggles with impulses to hold back or not to talk at all, or to rearrange his words into pleasanter and more acceptable forms; that is, into forms which are more flattering to his self-esteem and to the impression which he wants to make on the analyst. The mere presence of the silent analyst exercises a profound influence on this process. The intensity of this inner struggle varies from time to time. No patient achieves unguided speech continually. Usually, indeed, the psychoanalyst has to work for weeks or even months before he succeeds in ridding a patient of inhibitions which make free associations impossible. Since without free associations we cannot penetrate to unconscious levels, one of the primary functions of the psychoanalyst is to help the patient surmount the inner obstacles to the production of free associations. Throughout an analysis, indeed, the freedom with which such associations keep flowing is one of the important indicators of progress. In especially difficult cases certain drugs have been tried in an effort to help patients to overcome this difficulty. Their success has not yet been fully established; but it is well to bear in mind the fact that true free associations are not easily come by, and make up only a small portion of any analytic session.

The analytic work which is required to clear away the emotional obstacles to the production of free material turns out to be fruitful in many ways. Each time in the course of an analysis that it becomes necessary to resolve feelings which are obstructing free associations, an alteration occurs in the patient. Thus, even when the struggle to maintain the free production of psychological data turns some phases of an analysis into a pitched battle with the psychoanalyst, it leads to a deepening understanding of the patient's problems.

Patients have many special difficulties in producing free associations. There are those who cling to logic out of terror, as a frightened bather in the ocean clutches the ropes as he jumps up and down. There are those who exploit logic obsessionally, using it as their only weapon of attack and defense, under the spur of an unconscious hate. There are those who flee from free associations out of shame; shame at what they might say, fear lest free paths of thought would trap them into an admission of something they are ashamed to confess—(e.g., a man who had stolen from his father, a woman who had suffered from compulsive promiscuity, etc.). There are obstacles to free associations which arise from the symbolic values which words themselves, or the mere act of uttering them, may have for certain patients.

All such difficulties, and many more, have to be resolved in the course of the analytic work itself, and tax the skill and ingenuity of the analyst to the utmost.

Among these various obstacles to the processes of free association, two have special significance: (1) the complex anxieties which patients feel at giving themselves up to the processes of free association at all, and especially in the presence of another person (the inner nature of these anxieties will be discussed later); and (2) emotional storms which sweep over the patient in his relationship to the analyst. These, however, constitute major obstacles to freedom in all human relationships. This is one of the several reasons why self-analysis, even to the limited degree to which it is possible at all, cannot achieve by itself the same therapeutic goals as the analytic process in the presence of a human psychoanalyst, before whom the patient must have the humility to reveal himself, and on whom in conscious and unconscious fantasies the patient works out his problems. The analyst as a target for the patient's difficulties is therefore an essential ingredient in the therapeutic process.

The Impossibility of Recalling One's Own Free Associations

Certain theoretical and practical consequences result from this dependence upon free associations. The patient who is allowing his thoughts to flow in this unguided fashion soon becomes lost in the labyrinth of his own associations. It is as impossible for him to recall all of his scattered, interrupted, and fragmentary thoughts as it is to recall a long chain of nonsense syllables. If after each session any patient has a clear recollection of the sequences of his ideas, it is easy to show that they have been produced not freely but under the influence of some guiding preconceptions and purposes. The worker in academic psychology used to be trained in the classical techniques of the introspectionist and was supposed, thereby, to be able to observe and to report his inner psychological processes unmodified. Actually by the very process of systematic observation and report he automatically restricted the freedom of his associations. Therefore, in order to study the uncharted paths of associations, an observer must be present to note the patterns traced by the patient's productions, or else one must use some method of mechanical recording.

For this same reason not even the trained psychoanalyst can be his own analyst. One cannot simultaneously be the miner and the assayer. One cannot produce ideas freely and at the same time note them and evaluate them; since the act of observing and recording will in itself alter their sequence. For research purposes, these methods of mechanical recording are an indispensable adjunct to the human observer; but no matter how perfect the recording apparatus may be, for therapeutic purposes the human observer is essential. For this there are further reasons, which will be discussed in Chapter VIII.

From time to time orderly sequences of thought occur during the flow of free associations, the stream of ideas assuming a logical, narrative, chronological, or argumentative form, without interrupting deflections. The experienced analyst will be as suspicious of a stream of thought that is always fragmented as of one that is always carefully organized. But the patient who never produces free associations, never gets analyzed.

The Couch

The patient is usually requested to lie on a couch during most if not all of the analysis. The purpose of this is primarily to facilitate the production of the free associations which we have been discussing. It is necessary to conduct an analysis in the presence of a psychoanalyst; but it usually helps a patient to relax if he does not have constantly to observe the psychoanalyst and to adapt to his presence. When a patient is face to face with the psychoanalyst, it is inevitable that he will respond continually to the analyst's facial expressions and gestures. Whether the analyst shows his feelings in his expression or whether he maintains a stony immobility, the watchful patient will find meanings in it. This introduces distorting external impressions into a stream of thought which is most useful when it proceeds spontaneously from the patient's inner psychic life.

Furthermore, it is to the patient's advantage that the psychoanalyst should be relaxed, because only in this way can the analyst listen to the patient's productions with the greatest possible freedom. If the patient were merely to turn his back to the analyst while seated in a chair, the psychoanalyst could not observe him at all. If, on the other hand, the patient reclines on a couch, with the psychoanalyst sitting just behind the head of the couch, it becomes possible for both the patient and the psychoanalyst to be relaxed, at the same time affording the analyst an opportunity to observe the patient's gestures and his facial expression. Thus the analytic couch, about which there has been considerable discussion and perplexity, is actually a minor detail of psychoanalytic technique, nothing more mysterious than a helpful and sensible expedient.

It has one further value. By keeping out of the patient's direct line of vision, the analyst remains less "real" to the patient than he would become in the course of a long analysis, if this were conducted vis-à-vis. Therefore, the couch helps to preserve what has been called the analytic incognito, and thus increases the value of the analytic work on transference manifestations. These are discussed in Chapter VIII.

In spite of these considerations, however, the use of the couch is not indispensable. For various reasons some patients become completely blocked if they lie down. Some become panicky or depressed. In such cases the difficulty has to be analyzed before the couch can be used helpfully. Consequently, some patients vary between sitting up, walking around, and the couch. However, it is probably true that the ability to produce free associations fluently while on the couch is a fairly reliable index of analytic progress; and I would never feel entirely secure about an analysis in which the patient had never been able to use the couch.

The Direct Question vs. Free Association

The psychoanalyst makes only limited use of direct questions. There are times, of course, when these are essential, either for eliciting precise information or as a stimulus to further free associations. But for the most part it is better to allow the historical data of the patient's life and his opinions and feelings to express themselves spontaneously and without the guidance of systematic inquiry. This means a freer and at the same time a more disconnected and less orderly history than would be produced in response to leading questions. The reconstruction of such a history takes longer; but the historical data comes to light against a rich background of associations, which in turn give emotional significance to the bare facts. There are occasions, of course, when the psychoanalyst must use questions to gather facts, as with children, with families, and occasionally to corroborate or correct the data elicited from patients themselves. In general, however, the facts assembled through questioning can be used only as the patient elaborates upon them freely. Histories which are put together in response to persistent questions are in general shallow, as compared with histories which are compiled more slowly by the use of the method of free association.

"Homework" During the Analysis

During the course of an analysis a patient often asks whether or not he should think up things to talk about ahead of time, whether he should write them down, whether there is work that he should do outside, and whether he should read psychoanalytic literature. For all of these questions there are no generally binding rules; but the guiding principles are implicit in the foregoing discussion of the process of free association. Certainly, both in and out of the analytic session the patient is free to think or write anything that he pleases. It is essential only that when he comes to his analytic hour he should not confine his thoughts to the paths he has traversed already, but that even when he uses his previous thoughts or notes as a starting point, he should thereafter allow his associations to roam as freely as they please. Such "homework" is useful when it serves merely as a springboard from which the patient dives into his own free associations. Beyond this one may say that the amount of thought which a patient devotes to his analysis when he is away from it may be an index of the sincerity of his analytic purpose. On the other hand, either an obsessive preoccupation with the analysis or an extreme inability to think about it at all, are equally indicative of the presence of unresolved emotional problems which must be dealt with in the analysis itself.

The values and dangers of analytic reading vary with different patients and in different phases of each analysis, and in each case have to be determined as the work proceeds. This is often an issue of special importance in the training of young psychiatrists, who naturally are eager to read as much and as early as possible in the course of their training analyses. Experience has demonstrated, however, that it is usually well to limit such reading at first, and to postpone it until late in the analysis. Otherwise, a patient is likely to intellectualize the analytic process, and may unwittingly make his associations fit his reading. He will have greater confidence in the spontaneity of his own productions and in their freedom from suggestion if he has not read a great deal of theory before he has uncovered his own material.

Popular Misconceptions Concerning Introspection and Free Association

Psychoanalysis is often accused of making patients morbidly introspective. If true, this would be an important objection; therefore it must be considered in relation, first, to the approach to psychoanalysis, and second, to the process of psychoanalysis itself.

As will be seen in Chapter XIV, on the approach to analysis, every patient goes through a stage in his journey towards treatment during which he must be brought to a realization of the extent of his illness. During this phase he will inevitably become preoccupied with his problems and his symptoms, since it is only by allowing himself to think and feel about himself that he will finally accept the fact that he is ill and needs help. During this pre-analytic struggle the patient may well appear to be "morbidly introspective." Moreover, through the course of an analysis there will be recurrent phases in which the patient turns into himself emotionally, and struggles anew with his consciousness of illness and his realization of his own maladjustment. During each such struggle the "introspection" reappears. This, however, is both necessary and constructive, since, unless the patient is willing to face inner realities, no psychotherapy is possible, whether psychoanalytic or otherwise.

Between this and what may rightly be called "morbid introspection" there is a wide gulf. What common sense objects to is that form of introspection *which is itself a symptom of illness and not a phase of treatment.* It is a' form of obsessive and solitary rumination which moves in closed circles without ever reaching any goal. It does not lead to the frank acknowledgment of illness, the necessity for which we have emphasized, nor is it related to the process of free association which has been described above. Instead, it is an obsessional symptom, a distortion of the intellect in the service of unconscious emotional needs. Free associations, on the contrary, are used to dissect and break down such obsessive introspection, so as to make possible a more effective form of self-observation.

Patients who suffer from obsessive rumination will at times distort the analytic instrument through this morbid symptom. When this happens, the psychoanalyst uses it to give the patient further insight into the symptom with which he is struggling. It is fair to state, therefore, that despite the fact that psychoanalysis turns the attention of the patient on himself, it does so in a form which is fundamentally different from that profitless type of introspection which is itself a manifestation of neurotic illness. The most important evidence of the validity of this statement is the fact that a successfully analyzed patient becomes far less subjective than ever before, indeed less subjective than the average man.

Connected with this issue is the widespread notion that all those who have neuroses are "introverts." By this term the layman means people who are continuously charged with highly personal emotions, and who are concerned primarily and exclusively with their own thoughts and feelings. Actually there are many patients of whom quite the reverse is true, and of whom their friends and relatives say, "He's the last person in the world I would have expected to have a nervous breakdown. He always seemed so cheerful. He never seemed to worry about himself. He was always busy and active." A reluctance to let oneself face one's own thoughts and emotions may be just as serious a symptom of maladjustment, as an obsessive inability to pay attention to anyone but oneself. Therefore, although the popular condemnation of obsessive introspection is valid, this condemnation should not include the properly guided psychoanalytic study of psychological problems by means of the technique of free association.

Summary

It is fair to say, then, that psychoanalysis makes use of two primary processes. The first is to survey the play of unconscious psychological forces in the patient's free associations. The other is to show the influence of these unconscious forces upon the pattern of the patient's daily life and upon his relationships to other human beings. Consequently, the psychoanalyst himself plays a dual role. In one he maps out for the patient hitherto unrecognized psychological linkages. He describes in a quiet, friendly, impersonal manner the significant connections which he sees between the various components of the patient's free associations. Since these sequences of thoughts and feelings must ultimately refer to the patient's own life, the interpretation of them leads step by step to a deeper understanding of the patient's personality and history. The patient soon discovers, however, that this work does not proceed in an emotional vacuum. No matter how quietly impersonal the psychoanalyst remains, and no matter how little the patient knows about him in reality, the analyst soon becomes a storm-center for the patient's highly charged emotions. This indeed is the second major role of the analyst; and in order to make it possible for the patient to produce his associations freely, these stormy, personalized emotions must be analyzed with the patient. That is, they must be watched for, anticipated, and described to the patient, sometimes before he is aware of them himself; and they must then be resolved by making clear their sources. This is known technically as the analysis of the transference situation; and if it is neglected, the production of free associations soon ceases, and the analysis reaches an impasse. This process, i.e., the analysis of the transference, will be the subject of the next chapter.

Chapter VIII

THE ANALYSIS OF THE TRANSFERENCE

The Phenomenon of Transference

In psychoanalysis the word *transference* is used for the fact that in adult years our relationships to others are compounded of both conscious and unconscious elements, and that the unconscious elements consist largely of attitudes, needs, feelings, and purposes which are carried over (i.e. "transferred") unconsciously from the attitudes and needs and feelings and purposes towards others which we developed in infancy and early childhood.

A great deal of misunderstanding exists about "the transference," and the "analysis of the transference." It sometimes is pictured as something which is put over on the unwary patient, as a Machiavellian maneuver by which the analyst artificially induces in a patient a peculiar attachment to himself; as a method reserved for young and beautiful women and never used with the poor or the ugly or, for that matter, with men; as a highly pleasurable state of infatuation with the analyst; or as something which develops late in an analysis and only as the result of some mysterious and possibly malevolent, obscure or lecherous attitude of the analyst.

In every detail these notions about transference are false. In the first place, transferred feelings run the whole gamut of human emotions, including hate and fear, distrust, rivalry and envy, quite as much as "love, faith, and confidence." Secondly, "transference" is not a "method used in psychoanalysis." Psychoanalysis recognized and named it; but it is a universal phenomenon, which occurs in significant measure in every human relationship. Furthermore, this unconscious transference of feelings occurs spontaneously and from the onset of the analysis, out of preformed attitudes which exist in every patient before he ever comes for treatment. Although it evolves through many changing phases in the course of any analysis, one never needs to wait for transference to develop. It begins even when a patient starts to consider being analyzed, indeed before he has even met his analyst, with his dim fantasies of what the analyst is going to be like. Transference never has to be cultivated by any analytic artifice. Peculiar to psychoanalysis is only one fact, namely that in analytic therapy the transferred feelings are demonstrated to the patient and are studied with him and traced to their origins. The purpose of this is to make clear to the patient what parts of his conscious feelings are appropriate, and what parts inappropriate, and how these feelings have arisen out of earlier relationships. This is of great value to the patient, because it shows him how such transplanted feelings have the power to distort other human relationships. Consequently there is never a psychoanalytic treatment, be it of an old man or of a young woman, of adult or child, of rich or poor, ugly or beautiful, in which transference does not occur, and in which the transference is not analyzed.

Perhaps a few examples will make this clear.

A man came for help who was poor, homely, sick and in desperate need. Analysis was started at once; but it was many months before the risk of suicide and of complete mental disintegration had been averted. Because the patient's illness had destroyed his business and rendered him penniless, he was treated for nothing. For this he was sincerely grateful; yet in spite of his gratitude, day after day the patient exploded at the analyst with furious bitterness, resentment, hostility and fear. The violence of his feelings towards the analyst is hard to describe; yet for a long time its cause remained obscure. The analyst knew only that the patient had had equally violent and equally unprovoked emotional storms in many other relationships. Then one day the patient related a dream which suddenly brought back to his mind something which had occurred in the analyst's waiting room on the occasion of the patient's first preliminary visit. As the analyst had entered the waiting room with his hand outstretched to greet the patient, and before a word had been spoken by either man, the patient suddenly had the thought, "He has an impediment in his speech." Then, as he got up to shake the analyst's hand, he had repressed this fantasy, not to recall it until several months later, when during the stormy course of his analysis it came back to him in connection with his associations to his dream. Further associations brought to light the fact that the most important person in the early years of this patient had been an uncle, who had alternated between effusive affection for the patient and stormy angers against him. This uncle, long dead, had in fact suffered from the impediment in his speech which the patient had momentarily attributed to the analyst. From this and other data it became clear that even before he had entered the analyst's office, the patient had been prepared unwittingly to identify the analyst with his uncle; and it was this unconscious anticipation which had led him first to imagine that the analyst suffered from the uncle's speech defect, then to repress this notion, and then to feel towards the analyst the violent fear and hate which as a small child he had felt secretly toward his uncle. This led to the discovery of the fact that similar feelings had been transplanted into the patient's relationships to his wife's father and brother, to friends and teachers in school and college, to his business associates, and even to his own sons. The clarification of the source of these transferred feelings threw light on one of the roots of this man's illness, and eliminated one of the most disruptive forces in his life, making possible a spontaneous improvement in all his human relationships. This is an example of what psychoanalysis means by "the analysis of the transference." This is hardly the exploitation of a "transfer of affection to the analyst." Here hostile feelings were the transplanted and distorting force which had to be analyzed.

Again, there was an emaciated little woman of forty-eight, looking as though she were deep in her seventies, who would flare into savage rages at those to whom she was most deeply attached, and for whom she had worked loyally through many years. Inevitably, in the course of time, the same angers occurred in her relationship to the analyst. Through a series of steps it became clear that in each such flare-up, although the analyst was a man, she was reacting to him as she had to her mother. Thus one day, as this frail wisp of a woman shouted at the analyst in a towering rage, she suddenly became aware that she felt as though he was the living embodiment of everything that she had feared and hated in her own mother. This mother had in fact been a tyrannical and unfair woman; and the discovery of the fact that the patient's feelings about the analyst were derived from her feeling about her mother proved to her that the same process distorted many other relationships, and initiated a gain in insight which gradually freed her from this persistent and destructive residue of her childhood.

Or consider a beautiful, gifted yet tragic woman who for years was haunted by crippling anxieties and phobias. Like an automaton she would swing from love to hate and back to love again in her relationships with her husband, her children, her family, and her friends. Inevitably in the course of treatment she showed the same swings in her feelings towards the analyst. Through the study of the sources of these feelings, she came to understand that she was superimposing on the analyst the image of an older brother who had brought her up. The intonations, inflections, gestures and mannerisms of the analyst all reminded the patient of this brother, although no other person who had known the brother would have recognized the fancied resemblance. The gradual elucidation of the fact that her violent and inconsistent feelings about the analyst had nothing to do with him, led the patient to realize that the same transplanted emotions had distorted her relationships to her husband, her sons, and her friends; and that this had caused much of the havoc in her life.

Finally there was a beautiful young woman whose analyst was an attractive man, not more than ten years her senior. Here if ever was a situation for the conventional assumption that "the patient falls in love with the analyst." What actually happened was quite different. From the first day, because of a bitter lifelong rivalry with her four brothers, her relationship to this analyst was one of well-masked hostility. With exceptional cunning she would set traps to fool him, making up stories, inventing dreams, and often protesting a love for him which masked her deep and abiding hatred of all men. Fortunately he was taken in neither by her pretended affection nor by her bursts of violent rage, until finally his quiet detachment made it possible for her to see that her efforts to seduce him were part of her unconscious need to destroy all men, a need which had wrought devastation all around her. This discovery was the turning point toward health.

Thus, this process which analysts call "transference" can make a man treat a business associate as though he were his brother, an employer as though he were a father, a teacher as though she were a mother. It can make us behave in ways which may have been appropriate in childhood, but which are inappropriate in adult years. It is one of several forces which can lead people to hate those against whom they have no grievance, to love those for whom they have no valid basis for affection, to fear those who are no threat to them. By distorting the relationships between men, transference hampers and cripples the universal groping for maturity and for an integrated existence which all men seek. Therefore, it is important for sociologists and cultural anthropologists and for ethical and religious leaders to understand the destructive role of this universal process in human affairs. To learn how easily we can fool ourselves about both our loving and our hating is a humbling lesson which has profound significance for man in his struggle to become civilized.

Regardless of the age and sex of the psychoanalyst, the patient reacts towards him with patterns which are characteristic of his attitude towards men and women in general. All human relationships are compounded of various admixtures of yearning, plus the frustrations of this yearning which lead to anger, fear and sorrow. These feelings may exist even when they are masked or disguised. The psychoanalyst helps the patient to greater clarity by giving him insight into the ways in which these feelings work in him, the disguises which they may assume, and the distortions which they introduce into his relationships with his fellows. However, for a considerable period in every analysis it is chiefly as these feelings manifest themselves towards the veiled figure of the psychoanalyst that it is possible for the patient to recognize the unconscious and fantastic sources of these disturbing emotions. It is in this way that the analysis of the "transference" helps to clear the air not only within the analytic situation, but in all of the patient's life relationships as well.

That the transferred feelings could be exploited by an unscrupulous or untrained analyst is obvious. It is for this very reason, however, that analytic training is so exacting; and it is also for this reason, as will be explained below, that the skillful and scrupulous analyst avoids all social relationships with his patients.

The So-called "Negative Transference"

What has already been said should make it clear that the term "negative transference" refers only to a phase in the analysis during which the patient feels a conscious antipathy towards the analyst. This may be quite as valuable therapeutically as a phase of positive feelings.

Even in launching an analysis it is not always necessary for the patient to like the analyst. Some years ago a woman was referred to an able and experienced colleague, who happened to be an unusually mild and gentle man. Nevertheless, for reasons which had not been anticipated, the patient reacted to him with an immediate violent antipathy. To the patient this gentle analyst represented the embodiment of evil. She rushed from her first interview to telephone the referring colleague full of fury and outraged reproaches, and begged him to send her to someone else. For various reasons, however, she was prevailed upon to return to the same analyst the next day. For four successive days her antipathy continued unabated. Then it began to lessen, only to recur from time to time at lengthening intervals and with diminishing violence. In the meantime, however, under the whiplash of this overwhelming reaction, an immense amount of repressed and highly-charged fantasies about men in general was thoroughly ventilated. The patient's reward for not running away was that her analysis progressed with exceptional speed. Under these somewhat exceptional circumstances, the fact that the patient battled through her frantic terror and revulsion at the very start of the analysis probably saved her many months of polite but evasive sparring.

One does not deliberately risk so difficult a challenge at the start of an analysis, because the analyst cannot yet know enough about his patient to be in a position to clarify the reasons for any violent hostilities. In most instances, therefore, rage at the start would make it wise to shift the patient to someone with whom the patient could launch the analysis more calmly. The foregoing episode is nonetheless worth citing to emphasize a point of general significance: namely that a patient's positive or negative feelings about his analyst arise predominantly out of unconscious fantasies which the patient brings preformed into the analytical situation and then drapes around the analyst. Therefore whether the patient likes or dislikes an analyst is intrinsically of little significance to the outcome of the treatment. What is important is that the feeling must be thoroughly analyzed. Once analyzed, positive and negative feelings are of equal value for the solution of a neurosis. What is called a "negative transference" is not negative in the sense of vitiating the treatment. Only if negative feelings make it impossible for the patient to work with the analyst and to produce free associations in his presence, will they necessitate a change of analyst. It should be kept in mind that positive feelings towards the analyst, unless correctly analyzed, can create quite as formidable an obstacle to the production of free associations as do negative feelings.

The Dependence of the Analysis of the Transference upon the "Analytic Incognito"

From the point of view of the patient, the analysis of the transference is one of the most valuable of the experiences which his treatment brings him. The reason for this is simple. The psychoanalyst as an individual must be unknown to the patient. Therefore he keeps himself as much in the background as possible, out of clear focus and definition, quietly friendly, but always impersonal and reserved. He makes no show of his life, his work, his tastes, his pets, his family, his feelings, or his opinions. Insofar as this is humanly possible he remains a peg on which the patient can hang his conscious and unconscious fantasies. Consequently, feelings which seem to the patient to be reactions to the psychoanalyst are not about the analyst as he really is. They are rather the expression of feelings which the patient harbored long before he ever knew the analyst, and which under appropriate circumstances he could feel towards almost anyone. By being unknown to the patient at the start, and by maintaining throughout the analysis his formal reserve, i.e., his "analytic incognito," the psychoanalyst makes of himself a neutral sample of all humanity in the patient's emotional life. This is what gives value to the study of the origins of the patient's feelings. Towards the shadowy image of the psychoanalyst the patient experiences anxiety, anger, hate, affection, jealousy and the like. In the early phases of the analysis most patients are unaware of these feelings until the analyst points out some indirect or disguised expression of them. By demonstrating the existence of such groundless affects in the analytic relationship, it becomes possible for the psychoanalyst to prove to the patient that similarly unfounded storms can warp his relationships to other human beings. By unearthing the original sources of these feelings in early childhood, the analysis makes it possible to eliminate them, or at least to lessen their intensity and their influence.

If on the other hand the patient knows the analyst personally, or knows a great deal about him through mutual friends or relatives, or else comes to know a lot about the analyst during the course of the analysis, it becomes impossible to use the attitude of the patient towards the analyst to illuminate the sources of his buried feelings towards others. The more the patient knows about his analyst, the more firmly will the patient's feelings be anchored in reality; and feelings which are a composite product of unconscious fantasies and realistic knowledge about the analyst are difficult to use to increase the patient's self-knowledge. Since realities are obvious, they mask the subtler role of fantasy. Consequently, the more a patient knows about an analyst, the more difficult does it become to demonstrate the role which unconsciously transferred feelings play in his relationship to the analyst, and therefore to the world at large.

That is why it is essential for the patient that the psychoanalyst be a stranger about whose personality he knows as little as possible, and why it is unwise for a psychoanalyst to capitalize his social contacts and his friendships to build up his analytic practice; and finally why it is destructive to an analysis for an analyst to establish friendly social relations with a patient. It is only with an unknown figure that

the analysis of the transference can be used with full therapeutic effect.

The Analytical Incognito as a Protection for the Patient

Another important purpose which is served by the conventional formality and impersonality of the relation between
an analyst and his patient is to protect the patient from the
human frailties of analysts. In spite of the careful training
to which an analyst is subjected, and in spite of every effort to
reduce to a minimum any sources of confusion from his own
unconscious, an analyst is not, and cannot be, a saint. He
cannot achieve a state of disembodied contemplation, free
from all earth-bound cravings and lusts, invulnerable to frustration or deprivation, and devoid of anger. He is at best
a fallible human being, with his own weaknesses and pains;
and no matter how carefully he has been analyzed in the
course of his training, not all of his frailties will have been
eliminated. How then can the patient be protected from
these residual weaknesses? This is achieved by maintaining
a strict formality between patient and analyst in the therapeutic situation, and by the rigid exclusion of all business or
social relationships between them. Why this is so should be
clear. In any social relationship, we serve our own conscious
and unconscious emotional needs. If any social relationship
with a patient were to be meaningful the analyst would have
to bring his own needs into that relationship. If he did not,
the relationship would be a sham. Yet the moment that he
made any such conscious or unconscious demands, the relationship would serve two masters; and from that moment, in
any further efforts to analyze his patient he could not have the
same objectivity that he had before. It would become impossible for him to be certain whether he was serving the patient's
needs or his own. A single-minded concentration on the
patient's needs can be achieved only when the patient is to the
analyst only a patient. Once he becomes a friend, then the

patient's needs and the analyst's needs become inextricably mixed.   That is why the strict preservation of formality between the patient and the analyst serves the double purpose of giving the analysis of the transference its maximal usefulness for the patient, and of protecting the patient from the human needs which every human analyst must have.   The analyst has every right to serve his own needs elsewhere, but never at the expense of his patients, and therefore not through social relationships with his patients.

Chapter IX

THE ROLE OF DREAM ANALYSIS

The Quality of Dreams

Readers may be surprised that up to this point there has been no mention of the analysis of dreams, which usually receives much emphasis in discussions of psychoanalysis. In reality the exploration of dream material, while of great value, is only one ingredient in the complex technique of analysis: an ingredient used freely in some analyses, sparingly in others, and in varying degrees in the different phases of all. Dreams have always seemed fascinating and mysterious. The nightmares of childhood may retain their vividness throughout life. The conjunction of the possible and impossible in dreams keeps alive the old yearning to be able through them to prophesy the future. None of this, however, has anything to do with the use of the dream in analytic therapy. Here the analysis of the dreamed experience is conducted as soberly as is the analysis of a waking experience. Reality is woven into the fabric of a dream, just as fantasy weaves its way through actual events; and the differences between the psychological significance of dreams and of real events are relative rather than absolute. The analysis of the two yields much the same sort of information, although each has its own special advantages.

Certain questions about dreams are asked regularly. People want to know if everybody dreams, if we dream all the time, if we dream and then forget the dreams, why we forget them, why dreams can be so confused and fantastic, why a dream which lasted only a fraction of a second may take so long to tell, whether dreams "mean" anything, and the like. It is not possible to be dogmatic in answering all these questions; but certain facts are clear.

We do not know whether everyone dreams all of the time that he is asleep. This is possible; but it is equally possible that we dream only during the stages of falling asleep and of waking up; or it may be that it is possible to recall only the dreams which occur during these transitions. However this may be, it is certainly not the clarity or emotional intensity of a dream which determines whether or not the dream is remembered. Vivid dreams may be forgotten quite as often as vague ones. Everyone has had the experience of dreaming something in sharp detail, of waking with the dream clearly in mind and a determination to remember it, only to find that by the next morning it is completely gone, perhaps to return to memory suddenly a few days later. Evidently, even when a dream is clear and vivid, active forces of some kind must determine what is forgotten and what is recalled, and when. The therapeutic value of the analysis of dreams is largely a result of alterations which are produced in these forces by the process of analysis. Much of the research work on dreams deals with the nature of these opposing or "censoring" forces; how they distort the content of dreams through processes of displacement, condensation, compromise, and the symbolic representation of the sources of the dream, and how they determine whether a dream is forgotten or recalled.

Our memory of a dream always includes a lot of "filling-in." Hardly ever do we dream as much of any dream as we think we do. There are occasional epic dreams which are remembered in every detail, but even these often prove to be a synthetic product of clear fragments and conscious or unconscious secondary elaborations. Most dreams consist largely of a series of vivid and highly condensed tableaux, not unlike old-fashioned charades or living pictures, or a series of "stills" from a motion picture. A sequence of such images can flash across the screen of our thought-processes in a fraction of a second, but it may take half an hour to tell the story which they represent. This is due partly to the tedious process of putting into words the quality of a single word or gesture, partly to the time it takes to fill in the gaps between the clear flashes, and partly to the fact that a dream is a condensed way of saying many things at once. Together these features of the dream-process account for much of the apparent confusion of the dream. It is fortunate, however, that the confused and uncertain parts of any dream, and indeed the uncertainty itself, can be quite as meaningful in an analysis as are the clear elements.

Many special features of the thought process in dreams are a direct result of the fact that in the dream we think primarily by means of visual images. In this respect dream thinking resembles the thought process of the human child, and probably that of all lower animals. Certainly most of us recall the look of things more readily than we can recall their sound or taste or smell or feel. This is partly because form and color remain relatively constant, whereas other modalities of sensation are transitory experiences, which can less readily be re-experienced unaltered. Furthermore, vision is the only sensation which during sleep can be completely eliminated at the level of the sense organ, that is, at the source. This is done through darkness and by shutting the eyes. Sound, taste, smell, the various forms of touch and internal bodily sensations can never be excluded to the same extent during sleep. At best they are diminished by rendering them more or less constant, and by a process of central muting in the brain, which is called "Inhibition".* As a result, sounds are rarely heard clearly in dreams, but are usually represented by a thought of the sound; and taste and smell and bodily sensations are seldom experienced as such in dreams. None of these is totally excluded, but their roles are quite secondary to visual imagery, which is the principal language of the

* Cf. Kubie, L. S., and Margolin, S.: "The Process of Hypnotism and the Nature of the Hypnotic State", *American Journal of Psychiatry*, Vol. 11, pp. 611–622, March 1944.

dream process. This is why the dream is predominantly a visual hallucination. Furthermore, for most people the visual images of dreams consist largely of black, white and grey. Colors appear relatively rarely, and are usually limited to one color, which picks out some particular object for special emphasis. The physiological reasons for this are not known.

The Meaningfulness of Dreams

An understanding of the value of the interpretation of dreams requires a statement of certain elementary facts, most of which are obvious, but whose significance is often overlooked.

(a) The same physiological apparatus, the same brain, and the same human being is the instrument of the psychological processes in the waking state and in dreaming.

(b) The psychological processes of the dream serve the same purpose as do the psychological processes of the waking state. This purpose is primarily to discharge psychological tensions which accumulate in us during the day. Dreams may serve this purpose in many ways. Even combat dreams which waken us with terrifying hallucinations protect the dreamer from even worse states of tension. More often by discharging tension the dream enables us to remain asleep.

(c) The immediate instigator of the tensions which accumulate at night is the residue of the day's unfinished business. Each day brings some experiences which yield a quiet glow of satisfaction, and others which end unhappily, leaving behind them a bad aftertaste. Some of these daily events make us feel confident, relaxed, and reassured; others leave us shaken, uneasy, depressed, and frightened. Some give us a feeling of virtue; other episodes awaken feelings of guilt. Some leave behind them feelings of peace and good will; others stir deep tides of rage. If we could make an algebraic summation at the end of each day, we would find that some days add up to a contented frame of mind, and others to a deep and restless discontent. The former usually lead to a relatively dreamless sleep, the latter to restlessness or wakefulness, or to sleep which is broken by dreams.

Such dreams regularly begin as more or less disguised attempts to resolve the emotional residue of the preceding day. They are efforts to find happier endings for the day's pain. This is a basic psychological law,—what Freud called "the pleasure principle." Hollywood, too, puts a happy ending to an unhappy tale. The child who wakens from a nightmare makes up a happy ending to the dream so that he can go back to sleep. Long after a dispute in which we have been worsted, we continue to think up the crushing arguments that did not occur to us in time. The man who has taken a beating in a fight thinks afterwards of all the blows he should have landed. The nation that has lost a war dreams of revenge.

This is precisely what happens at the end of the day. First come the spontaneous reveries which take possession of us as we drift off to sleep. Then comes the dream process, which begins as a continuation of these reveries. As we drift off to sleep, however, these gradually lose their anchorage in external reality. In spite of the fact that our thinking becomes increasingly fantastic as sleep deepens, it continues to serve the same psychological purpose. Automatically, therefore, as we slip away into sleep, our thought processes revolve around those problems which have been brought to the forefront of our minds and hearts by the less happy events of the preceding day. This is why the springboard from which every dream starts is the residue of the day's misadventures. Day-dreams are efforts to solve fragments of these problems. Sleeping dreams are condensations of many fragmentary day-dreams, which through sleep have lost their moorings in reality, but which continue the same old search for a happy ending.

(d) This does not mean that the dream process deals with trivial disappointments. On the contrary, those frustrations which are sufficiently highly charged to upset us, derive their emotional importance from the fact that they represent deeper struggles. The unhappy occurrences of each day are merely the most recent of a long line of earlier experiences which have sensitized us. Therefore, although every dream starts from the unhappy residue of trivial current experiences, it represents a condensation of our past. Every person and place and event in a dream is a fused image of people and places and events from many periods in the dreamer's life, plus the inner problems with which these are connected. Indeed these condensations can be so all-inclusive that the drama of a lifetime may be recaptured in one series of vivid and fantastic dream images. Hence every dream has not one but many "meanings." This is a further cause of the apparent confusion of dreams. Yet because of this condensation, the successful analysis of a dream uncovers a rich vein of gold, leading back from the present to remote and more deeply buried sources of trouble. Therefore the tracing of a dream to its immediate source in the trivial hurts of the preceding day is merely a first step towards an understanding of the experiences which have sensitized the dreamer to pain in the past. It is this which led Freud to call dreams the "Royal Road to the Unconscious."

Summary

One may summarize in general terms the present state of psychoanalytic theory of dreams. What we dream seems sometimes to be quite orderly and clear, and at other times wholly confused. In either case, the obvious content of the dream, technically known as the "manifest content", always represents much more than itself. By various technical procedures this can be deciphered and the "latent" or underlying significance of the dream can then be brought to light. When this is done the dream is seen to represent many buried feelings, wishes and problems about which the dreamer is so deeply in conflict that he cannot become aware of them by conscious introspection. Each dream, then, is an attempt to solve unconscious conflicts which were touched off by experiences of the preceding day, but which had their origins in those earlier struggles of infancy and childhood, which have become inaccessible to conscious introspection. In the compromises, displacements, and symbolic imagery which constitute the dream, the early emotional and instinctual struggles are represented in condensed visual images. These fundamental conflicts are the power source of the dream. They are like the field of force between magnetic poles: the residues of the unhappy experiences of the preceding day arranging themselves along the lines of force like iron filings in a magnetic field. The interpreter uses them to discover the shape and character of the field of force, i.e., of the fundamental problems and conflicts which are latent in the dream.

Chapter X

THE CHOICE OF A PSYCHOANALYST

*The Influence of Individual Differences such as Personality,
    Age, Sex, etc.*

It often is asked how much difference it makes who
psychoanalyzes a patient, or whether the same results will be
achieved no matter who conducts the analysis. This question is of concern to every prospective patient who naturally
wants to know how he can be reasonably sure of finding the
analyst who will be "right" for him.

The first step is to consult the nearest recognized psychoanalytic society or Institute (see Appendix) in order to ascertain whether the man who is being considered is a member
of an accredited psychoanalytic society and has been trained
at a recognized Institute. In this way one may at least be sure
not to fall into the hands of someone who is untrained. That
there are differences in skill among various members of any
such group is inevitable, just as there are among the members
of a society of surgeons; and opinions will differ concerning
the relative skills of various members. Nevertheless, membership in a psychoanalytic society guarantees a minimal
level of intelligence, integrity, and specialized training.
Beyond that, the prospective patient must depend upon the
advice of physicians and friends who may know something
of the work and reputations of different analysts. It is reassuring, however, that minor differences in skill have less influence than is generally supposed on the success or failure of
an analysis.

Assuming, then, that only analysts who have been adequately trained are under consideration, the question remains
what differences in the course of the analysis and in its therapeutic outcome will result from differences in the personali-

ties of various analysts. The effects of personality traits have to be considered separately in relation to three phases of an analysis: (1) the initial steps of the analysis; (2) the analytic process in full swing; and (3) its ultimate results. In the introductory steps and in the early phases of the work, the analyst's sex, voice, manner, appearance, and other individual peculiarities evoke specific responses. Consequently, the beginning of the ascent of the analytic mountain will take a path with any analyst which would not be identical with the path along which some other analyst would guide the patient. Issues will arise and obstacles will be surmounted in different sequences. Naturally it is easier to launch an analysis when a patient's first response to the analyst is comfortable and full of confidence. However, I have seen analyses work out successfully, even when the patient's initial reaction was one of blind hostility, panic and distrust. (An example of this is given in Chapter VIII.)

As the treatment proceeds, however, if the analysis is conducted by a man who is careful to remain as unobtrusive and inconspicuous as possible, the effects of superficial differences gradually disappear. Behind the mask of the analytic incognito, the personal quirks of the individual analyst become inconspicuous through habituation, and lose most of the emotional significance they may have had at the start. Consequently, the personality of the analyst becomes progressively less important than the fantasies with which the patient invests him. In the end, the view from the top of the mountain will be the same, however much the paths up the mountains might have differed had a different analyst been the guide. This will be true, however, only if the analyst conscientiously maintains his "analytic incognito." (cf. Chap. VIII.)

Indeed, if the analyst remains inconspicuous, in most instances the influences even of his sex may be disregarded; and whether the analyst is a man or a woman, old or young, will make little difference in the ultimate outcome, even when it has made a considerable difference in launching the analysis and in the order in which the patient's material comes up. Again, this is because the patient's fantasies can treat the same analyst sometimes as a man and sometimes as a woman, sometimes as old and sometimes as young, irrespective of the actual facts. Therefore the naive idea that all male patients should go to male analysts and all women patients to women, need be given little serious consideration.

To this general rule, however, there are certain exceptions. For instance, in the treatment of certain psychosexual problems, the sex of the psychoanalyst may be quite important. In such cases, however, it is not always possible to predict which will be better. In the course of the analysis, a male analyst will sometimes find it advisable to send his patient to a woman analyst or vice versa, in order to facilitate the clarification of some special aspect of the patient's problems. This will involve a temporary loss of momentum in the work and a short period of recapitulation; but after such a change the two pieces of analytic work will quickly fit together.

We have already emphasized the necessity of going to a psychoanalyst who, apart from his professional reputation, is unknown to the patient personally. It may be hard to convince patients of the importance of this rule. Patients are usually frightened at the mere prospect of being analyzed; and the fact that it will seem easier to most patients to start with someone they know and in whom they have confidence, leads them to think that it will be easier all the way through. Prospective patients cannot foresee the difficulties that knowing the analyst will create for them as the treatment develops. It should be understood that these future difficulties are for the patient, and not for the analyst. The material in Chapter VII (on free association) and in Chapter VIII (on transference) will have made clear the reasons for this. Consequently a conscientious analyst will refuse to analyze not only his own friends and relatives, but even their intimate friends,

since these would inevitably have learned a good deal about
the private life and personality of the analyst from the
casual conversations of their mutual friends or relatives.
The careful analyst will consent only to guide them into the
hands of competent colleagues.

The major responsibility for adhering to this rule falls on
the analyst; but the patient who comes to an analyst asking
to be analyzed and who is refused, feels deeply hurt at the
rejection, and finds it hard to understand or even to believe
the analyst's explanation. It will lessen this hurt if the
patient understands that in turning him over to a colleague
the analyst is merely following a practice which applies to
all patients because its value has been proved repeatedly.

There are times, however, when it is impossible to adhere
strictly to this rule. A very disturbed patient may refuse to
go to anyone else. The family physician or the responsible
relative may take a similarly intransigent position. Under
these circumstances, especially when there is danger that
delay might allow the illness to get out of hand, the analyst
may be forced to take into treatment even a relative or friend,
if only temporarily. Usually, he will at once begin to prepare that patient for an ultimate transfer to some colleague
who is unknown to the patient. He will try to do this within
a few weeks but there are occasions when for technical reasons
it may take months to accomplish it.

Concurrent Treatment of Patients who are Friends or Rela- tives of Each Other

Similar considerations must be weighed whenever the question arises whether to treat concurrently or in close succession two intimate friends or two members of one family.
Here no unvarying rule can be laid down; but whenever
possible this is to be avoided. Analytic work is difficult
enough without going out of our way to complicate it unnecessarily, by adding the competitive jealousies which are certain
to arise between any two patients who know each other well.

No two analyses progress with equal speed; and each patient is likely to watch the progress of the other with an anxious eye, at times unhappy, at times triumphant, depending on who seems to be out in front at the moment. Even the patient who seems to gloat over his friend's tribulations will at the same time have his own confidence shaken by the other's upsets. To some extent all of this can be used as grist for the analytic mill; but it tends to focus attention on the intra-analytic struggle, and to obscure those problems which are indigenous to the patient's life. Furthermore, in such situations patients are likely to lose their confidence that what they say is for the ear of the analyst alone. A nagging doubt arises as to whether the analyst has carried tales from one to the other. Nor will it be easy for the analyst himself always to be sure which of two patients has given him which version of episodes in which both patients have been involved. Consequently in his discussion of events with either patient, the analyst may involuntarily betray one to the other. Thus the analyst may find that he has given the appearance of taking sides, which will end his therapeutic usefulness to one or the other patient, or both. It should be emphasized that these complications add to the difficulties of analysis for the patients, not for the analyst. Such complications should, therefore, be avoided by observing the simple rule of not analyzing two close friends or relatives simultaneously.

Even to analyze relatives or close friends in quick succession is not without some risks of this nature. There may be an unfair pressure on the first to finish up in a hurry so as to make room for the second. Should he then need to return, he may find the path blocked. Furthermore, as time goes on, the analytic incognito cannot remain wholly intact, since as he goes through his analysis any patient inevitably if gradually picks up a certain amount of personal information about the analyst. Late in the analysis this will make relatively little difference; but the friend or relative who follows can learn more about the analyst from his analyzed friend than is good for an analysis which is just beginning. Such considerations as these should be taken into account whenever this issue arises.

The Austere Code of the Psychoanalyst

For all these reasons, as well as those presented in Chapter VIII, it follows that throughout the course of the treatment, the patient and the analyst will eschew all social or business contacts outside of the analysis, so as to maintain the analytic incognito as intact as possible. Therefore, the conscientious psychoanalyst is not free to expand his practice by social contacts with the friends and relatives of his patients, as is entirely proper for other physicians. The analyst must subject his personal advantage to the needs of his patients, and practice his particular medical specialty with a code which is more austere in this respect than that which is necessary for other medical and surgical disciplines.

Chapter XI

THE RELATIONSHIP OF THE ANALYSIS TO THE PATIENT'S LIFE DURING THE COURSE OF TREATMENT

The Pledge

Before the start of an analysis it is customary for the analyst to advise the patient that for the duration of the treatment he should attempt not to make any basic changes in his life, until the actual and immediate necessity for the change and its unconscious meanings have both been thoroughly explored. This restriction applies to such matters as homes, jobs, occupations, schools, marital status, etc.

There are two reasons for imposing this limitation on a patient's freedom during an analysis: one is to protect the patient's own best interests, the other is to make sure that fundamental psychological problems will not escape analysis. No such rule would be needed, were it not for the somewhat surprising fact that so many human beings find it less disturbing to act than to think; and once a patient has acted, it becomes extremely difficult and often impossible to lead him to re-examine the subtle conflicts out of which his action arose. Furthermore, without an agreement not to act in the dark, such patients may endanger their health, their lives, their careers, and their most important human relationships through impulsive behavior, which may be a transient product of the analytic process itself. Therefore this single analytic restriction on a patient's liberty is justified, because it both facilitates the analysis and protects the patient during the analysis.

There are other patients, of course, for whom no such rule is needed, because their personalities are so organized that they are frightened more easily by doing than by thinking. These patients often try to use the analysis as an excuse for doing nothing, and for postponing action in all the major and minor issues of their lives. Unless delay might bring such a patient into critical danger, the analyst can usually wait for the analysis of this patient's anxieties to release him for spontaneous and effective action.

Setting the Stage for Analysis

In planning the analysis of a child or adolescent it frequently is possible to make substantial changes in the setting of the patient's life for the duration of the analysis, changes which are designed specifically to facilitate the progress of the treatment. Only rarely can this be done with adults, however. This is partly because they usually come for analysis burdened with responsibilities which cannot be delegated to others even temporarily, and partly because low-cost neurosis treatment centers where patients could live cheaply during the early stages of analysis do not yet exist. In fact, merely because it is not easy to make the necessary changes, far too little thought has been given to the problem of how to set the stage for an analysis so as to launch it under the best possible circumstances.

Patients come to analysis with their lives badly snarled; they are unhappy and defensive over the pain which their neurotic conduct has cost others, and often in need of protection, especially at the start, from the resentments which their illness has aroused. All too often the analyst discovers that he is dealing not with the neurosis of the patient alone, but with complex neurotic states of those with whom the patient's life is interwoven. To sort all of this out, and to make the patient see where his neurosis ends and those of others begin is never easy. It becomes simpler to do this if the patient can be transplanted temporarily to a neutral and relatively impersonal atmosphere. From this vantage point it is possible for the patient to look back upon his life with some degree of objectivity and perspective.   It is human to be less defensive about the past than about current confusions and mistakes.

Before there were any analysts in America, patients had to go to Europe for analysis.   The Atlantic Ocean separated them from much of the confusion of their daily lives; and they could then analyze this confusion from a helpful distance in time and space.   However, this had one obvious disadvantage, namely that the analysis could not continue when the patient returned to his home.   During the recent war, the armed services also recognized the need for treatment facilities which would help the patient to a perspective on the situation in which his illness had arisen.   For this purpose special neurosis treatment centers of various kinds were organized, not as psychiatric hospitals, but as camps in which patients could receive psychiatric treatment while maintaining an appropriately reduced level of military activity.   In civilian practice the need for such centers is barely recognized.   There have been some moves in this direction, sufficient perhaps to demonstrate its importance, such as the Cassel Hospital in England, and especially the Austen Riggs Foundation in Stockbridge, Massachusetts.   Many more are needed, especially in connection with general hospitals, and on a self-sustaining and economical basis.

There are other subtler and more powerful reasons why it would frequently be helpful to have a patient start his analysis in such an ivory tower, out of reach of the stresses and turmoils of his daily life, and with a moratorium on all daily problems, where no issues would press for immediate decision and where he would live for a time without external demands, deprivations, frustrations, or frictions.   Since there would be no immediate external stresses, any unhappiness which he experienced and any symptoms which occurred would obviously have to be traced to residues from the recent or remote past.   Consequently the role of his unconscious conflicts would become evident to the patient much more quickly and vividly than is possible when a patient can use his current problems as a smoke-screen to hide the past.

Later, when such a patient returned to his home to complete his analysis, he would bring to his old problems the insights which he had gained in the ivory tower, insight into the continuing influence of his own past, insight into the structure of his own personality, and insight into the reverberations of his old unsolved and hitherto unconscious conflicts in his present life.

I think of a patient with whom chance made it possible to conduct his analysis in just such a series of steps. The analysis began far from his family and friends, and with no work responsibilities. After some time, in graded doses, he started back to work. Then he reached out for some friendly social contacts with new acquaintances. Still later he began to see something of his family and old friends, until finally he resumed his full domestic responsibilities, including the challenge of a difficult marriage. It is only rarely, however, that it is possible to arrange so precise a sequence of events. Usually, as a matter of fact, it is only during a retrospective survey of an analysis that the analyst would understand enough about a patient to know how to plan such a schedule wisely.

In the workaday world which the analyst and the patient share, all of this is scrambled together: the past, the present, and the future, the old buried sources of difficulty, and the immediate external trials and tribulations. It is conceivable that as new types of neurosis treatment centers are developed, it will be possible to approximate the ivory tower during the introductory steps in the analyses of rich and poor alike. At present, however, this hope is only a blue-print for the future.

Analyst or Guide

Experience has proved that it is not possible for the analyst to advise and guide a patient in his practical affairs without seriously undermining his value as analyst. There are many reasons for this. First of all, direct advice automatically limits the spontaneity and freedom of the patient's associations. Furthermore, in the process of advising the patient the analyst reveals himself to some degree as a real person, since his advice will disclose his standards, his tastes, his own ideas about how life should be lived, and his moral judgments. Inevitably the patient's subsequent productions will be colored by these disclosures. The effect may be slight at first, but the cumulative influence of continual guidance can only distort and mask the expression of the patient's problems. Similarly, if the analyst should attempt actively to influence the patient's conscience, he will lose still further his analytic incognito and his impartial detachment. This will again deprive the patient of a part of the psychological freedom which is essential if analysis is to penetrate to unconscious levels. To the extent to which this occurs, the patient's associations conform to an imposed stereotype, and lose their value as clues to his own unconscious attitudes and feelings.

Furthermore, towards the analyst who plays the role of a parental guide the patient will ultimately react with both the automatic submissiveness and the automatic rebelliousness characteristic of the child. In "obedient" phases of the analysis the rebellion will be masked. A sham compliance will simulate an improvement which will break down again as soon as the more independent and rebellious phases of the patient's responses assert themselves. Yet without this ultimate rebellion against the analyst who has presumed to interfere, the patient's final independence will be jeopardized. The more actively authoritarian the analyst has been, the more impossible will it be for him to analyze with the patient the fantastic transference roots of either his submissiveness or his rebelliousness.

For all of these reasons, the psychoanalyst cannot often give a patient advice and guidance without impairing his analytic value. In general, therefore, his role is to allow wise decisions to grow spontaneously in the patient, as a gradual outcome of the analytic work, and with a minimum of advice.

Obviously, where a patient is too sick to be entrusted with the freedom to make decisions for himself, or where there is a strong tendency towards impulsive and dangerous acts, someone may have to serve as counsellor and guide, or even as a custodian. In such cases, however, it is best for the analysis if this function is performed by someone other than the analyst. Sometimes this guardian can be a member of the family, sometimes another psychiatrist, sometimes the family physician, sometimes a nurse working under the analyst's direction. In general, however, for the reasons given, the analyst divorces himself as completely as possible from direct control of the patient's life.

The Basis of Active Interference During Analysis

There are exceptions to all such rules. For various reasons the analysis itself may sometimes require direct or indirect interference with a patient's life, his habits, and his relationships with people. This occurs chiefly in the service of two fundamental but little understood requisites for successful treatment: i.e., the need to accept deprivation and to face anxiety.

(a) The Principle of Deprivation

In the treatment of neurotic problems easy victories rarely last; and during his treatment every patient must be prepared to face periods in which his only gratification will be a slow and barely perceptible growth in understanding. This demands of the patient the ability to wait; and the patient who cannot tolerate even this degree of deprivation, who demands quick results and immediate gratifications, cannot be psychoanalyzed unless and until this attitude can be altered. Moreover, so important is this principle of deprivation that the psychoanalyst must sometimes intervene to cut off or limit even normal sources of satisfaction in the patient's life, so as to force the patient into a state of active need.

That same school of Russian physiologists which gave to psychoanalysis the experimental proof of the validity of the method of free association (cf. Chapter VII) furnished valuable support for this other fundamental principle as well. They demonstrated that it is only in a state of craving that important new connections can form in the central nervous system. The psychoanalytic version of this fact is Freud's observation that an analysis makes best progress in the presence of deprivation. Consequently when there seem to be no fundamental deprivations in a patient's life, the analyst may have to introduce them. The form which this will take varies with every patient and in different phases of every analysis. For one person it may mean living away from home; for another giving up reading or the movies; another who hides his problems in a compulsive work drive may have to take a vacation from work; a fourth may have to give up a favorite sport or stop even moderate drinking; a fifth may have to avoid normal social life with friends and family. What is cut off will depend on which activity has been used persistently as a major escape from inner problems.

It is difficult to apply this principle skillfully, without being either too lenient or too severe. As much as any other analytic maneuver this puts to a test the analyst's own normality, his analytic understanding of his own unconscious, and his freedom from anxiety and from unconscious hostility. Furthermore, whenever an analyst intervenes actively in a patient's life, he finds that the practical consequences involve not the patient alone, but also all of those with whom the patient's life is interwoven. For this reason, it may be necessary to explain the matter in some detail. Otherwise the analyst may find himself warring with a mystified and resentful circle of family and friends. (Cf. Chapters XII and XIII.)

(b) *Uncovering Hidden Anxieties and Masked Symptoms*

The second reason for active intervention in the daily life of a responsible adult patient is the need to uncover anxieties or other mood disturbances, which without such intervention might remain masked. This never applies to painful neurotic symptoms. Of these every patient wants to rid himself. But many important manifestations of the neurotic process are not painful to the patient himself; and in the defense of these subtler difficulties the patient runs from cover to cover, seeking to hide all revealing symptoms and moods. It is a significant human trait that when dealing with organic disease we so frequently try to prove how sick we are physically; whereas when dealing with neuroses we try to prove how much better off we are than our doctors, friends, or families maintain. A patient may come to an initial consultation only to find himself compelled quite unexpectedly to make light of his difficulties. Not infrequently he may actually be unable even to remember the symptoms which brought him. The same automatic defense against the acknowledgment of neurotic illness continues to operate recurrently throughout the whole course of treatment. The patient may attempt to minimize his symptoms to his analyst while trying at the same time to over-dramatize them to his friends. Consequently, the psychoanalyst must often dig out the elusive evidence of illness from an evasive patient. This he does by cutting off all of the masking devices which the patient has been in the habit of using. Unless the analyst succeeds in this, the patient may be able to fool himself and his friends, as well as the analyst, with an illusion of health which will last only as long as the treatment.

Certain implications of this are especially important. Thus, it is traditional and legitimate for most physicians to play a pacifying, reassuring and comforting role towards their patients. The psychoanalyst, on the other hand, must often do just the opposite. He will be tactful and judicious in his warnings, but in the end he must be merciless in forcing a patient to face his neurosis. Indeed, just as he must sometimes intervene actively to produce situations of deprivation, so he often has to tumble the patient into those very situations which arouse his fears, depression and anger. In some illnesses, the need for this is so clear that even the casual onlooker will understand. Thus it is evident that at some point in the course of the treatment a patient with a phobia of high places must be encouraged to go up to face this fear; or that a patient with a handwashing compulsion must at some point restrain his ritual, no matter how much anxiety this may cost him. In such maneuvers the analysis meets with no objections from the patient's family and friends. On the contrary, they have had to endure so many inconveniences from the patient's symptoms and eccentricities, that if they hear about the analyst's recommendation, they welcome it approvingly. Their attitude is, "It's about time someone made him stop that nonsense."

There is always a long preliminary period, however, before any such recommendation can be made. The psychoanalyst must learn the meaning of the particular symptom, or of the disturbing way of life, and this knowledge must have been shared with the patient, before such intervention is possible. Therefore, each symptom must be allowed to play its part in the analysis, as it has previously existed in the life of the patient. The soldier who never goes into battle never gets killed; and the symptoms that never appear actively in the analysis never are analyzed.

During this long period of waiting, the interested onlookers may well become impatient and critical. They begin to complain, "Why doesn't he do something? Why doesn't he stop that? What good is all this talking, anyhow?" To this the only answer is that premature interference will fail, and will also prejudice the value of any later efforts to intervene. Therefore the wise psychoanalyst waits patiently, and it is a fatal error to allow himself to be hurried by the impatience of family or friends.

Unfortunately the task of the psychoanalyst is rarely confined to maneuvers the wisdom of which is evident to the onlooker. Frequently the patient's problems lurk behind

seemingly unrelated details of his life. Where these involve
no one but the patient, the analysis deals with them without
reference to the outside world. Thus no one but the patient
and his psychoanalyst is aware that anything has happened
when some detail of a patient's patterns of sleeping, or eating
or dressing has been altered in the effort to unmask obscure
anxieties.

It is a different matter, however, when important human
relationships or the patient's occupation must be interfered
with. It is not easy for old friends to find themselves out of
bounds, much less for those relatives or the physician who
may have spent years struggling over the patient's health.
Yet the analysis sometimes is forced to act as a wedge temporarily separating the patient from these very relationships.
To those who are excluded this seems like inexplicable ingrat-
itude, just one more evidence of the unreasonable nature of
the whole procedure. Yet the good intentions of these well-
wishers have little to do with the use which the patient may
make of their loyalty. It is as impossible to create self-sustaining health for a patient who is constantly being propped
up, as it would be to strengthen a limb which is kept in a cast.
For this reason, if for no other, it may be necessary during
an analysis to lead a patient through a period of relative isolation from those on whom he has depended in the past.

Ultimately, the successful analysis will bring the patient
back again to renewed closeness to all whose intimacy
has stood the test of analytic scrutiny, and where the basis
of the relationship has proved to be fundamentally normal.
The path to this goal may be long and tortuous, however, and
requires an unusual degree of patience and confidence.

(c) *Dealing with the Neurotic Exploitation of Normal Life*

Sometimes the analyst may even take a parent or a child
temporarily out of his own home, or a man away from his
occupation. This may become necessary precisely because

men sometimes hide their emotional difficulties in their most normal activities and relationships: making their lives endurable and masking their anxieties through an unconscious exploitation of relatives and friends, of work and play. When this is true, the psychoanalyst is forced to strip away these masking devices one by one, until the difficulties which the patient is hiding are revealed. If these devices were always in themselves abnormal or unnatural there would be relatively little difficulty about doing this. Unfortunately, however, what one man hides in compulsive drinking, another man may hide in an excessive work drive, or a woman in hyperconscientious preoccupation with her family and children, or in bridge, or philanthrophy or society. Obviously no one will doubt the wisdom of interfering with the habits of the drinker; but it seems strange to the onlooker when the analyst interferes even temporarily with the others. Nevertheless, where practical considerations make it impossible to limit such activities, the analysis may be seriously hampered.

The ideal analytic situation is one in which the patient can be brought to understand the need for this type of self-denial, and will impose it on himself of his own accord, and without active pressure from the psychoanalyst. Difficult problems may arise when a patient persistently refuses to accept all such deprivations, and is reluctant to face anxiety or pain in any form. This, indeed, is one of the factors which can make it peculiarly difficult to analyze successfully a patient who is absorbed in a love affair, or who has great wealth. No human being accepts deprivation readily, and where the consolations of love or wealth or successful work are easily available, it takes a patient of exceptional stamina to turn his back upon them. It is characteristic of analyses of the affluent that they are frequently interrupted by self-indulgences —a trip to Florida, a hasty marriage, a hunting trip, etc. One unfortunate man who sought help for psychic impotence and attacks of overpowering anxiety, ultimately refused analysis because his wife was disappointed on learning that during the course of the analysis he might be unable to accompany her on their periodic hunting and fishing expeditions.

An analysis, therefore, may from time to time become involved in a struggle against a patient's methods of garnering the momentary pleasures with which he has been accustomed to mask his fear, anger, depression, and the like. In his effort to unmask hidden difficulties the psychoanalyst must at times block even healthy outlets of love and work and play, while at the same time, and paradoxically, allowing a patient to skirt danger or even to flounder into it if there is no other way to prove to him the neurotic basis of his conduct.

(d) *The Essential Conflict Between the Needs of the Analysis and the Immediate Desires of the World Outside*

The little world which circles around the outskirts of every analysis finds it hard to understand any of this. Its purposes are often directly opposed to the needs of the analysis. It is always trying to reduce the tensions which the analysis must sometimes inflate. It is outraged in those phases of the analysis which may isolate the patient from daily realities, i.e., from work, family, friends, society, or play; and it may be equally perplexed at those other moments when it becomes essential for the patient to have the closest possible contacts with these situations.

Similarly this small world always hopes that the psychoanalyst will intervene quickly to cut the patient's Gordian knots. In contrast to this "practical" point of view, when a patient is in a state of obsessional indecision, whether it be over buying a hat or contracting a marriage, the analysis tries to defer all impulsive pseudo-solutions of the problem. At such a juncture, to postpone acting may take courage and the ability to stand deprivation and uncertainty, until the psychic tension which is mobilized will bring into the open the unconscious forces out of which the paralyzing indecision has arisen. Therefore, the psychoanalyst must turn a deaf ear to the importunities of the outside world, when it says, *"Oh, why doesn't he tell him what to do—he must know by now—it would be better to do anything, just to get the suspense over."*

Here again we see that when dealing with an adult patient whose illness does not make him wholly irresponsible, the psychoanalyst cannot play the role of guide and protector without masking those inner problems which it is his primary function to uncover and resolve. Important plans and decisions may grow out of the analytic work, but, except as a temporary measure, they cannot be imposed by the analyst if he has his patient's ultimate independence at heart. It is only in dealing with children, or with psychotic patients who are not fully responsible, that the psychoanalyst must either take on this double role himself (which may seriously hamper his analytic function), or else turn over to others the role of custodian and guide.

Chapter XII

THE RELATIONSHIP OF THE OUTSIDE WORLD TO PATIENTS UNDER ANALYSIS

The Patient's Self-Protective Secrecy

A patient often enters analysis determined to tell no one of his plans. Sometimes this is because he realizes that if he took anyone into his confidence the news would gradually reach the ears of others who would gossip about it, or who might even try to interfere. A patient is wise to avoid being drawn into futile arguments when his undivided attention is needed for the analysis itself. At such times some measure of discreet silence, at least until the analysis is well under way, is sensible. However, secrecy can also arise from an unnecessary sense of shame. Because he fails to realize how universal are neurotic difficulties such as his, the patient feels mortified at any public acknowledgment of his need. He often pretends to himself that no one knows of his condition, and may try to hide the fact that he is in treatment, even when every close friend and relative is aware of his illness, and is hoping that he will have the courage to face it and to seek help for it. Not infrequently a patient will go to great lengths to hide an illness which everyone has long since recognized, even rejecting the treatment which he may need desperately. In a successful analysis such false pride and unnecessary shame will gradually be eliminated.

Frequently the patient who resolves to keep his analysis secret does so because his own doubts about analysis make him fearful of the skepticism of others. Here again, as the analysis proceeds and as anxieties lessen, friends and relatives gradually are taken into the patient's confidence. In this way, a little world of interested spectators slowly gathers around almost every psychoanalytic venture. The behavior of these onlookers, individually and collectively, can make a great difference to the comfort of the patient during his analysis and to his freedom from distracting external influences.

Any hot-house protection for psychoanalytic patients is neither possible nor desirable; but the patient has a right to a decently respectful attitude of non-interference. Patients go through phases of great emotional sensitivity. It was no act of kindness for a friend to call across a formal dinner table, "I can't believe you're having an analysis. You're young. You're attractive. Are you in love with someone else? Are you out of love with your husband?" How could the patient answer such an attack? How could she speak of the years of misery which she had always kept hidden? Nor was that other "friend" considerate who said, "Darling, I hope you're enjoying a perfectly lovely transference", to a patient who was in a turmoil of confused rage and terror in her attitude to the psychoanalyst. Such jibes are deeply hurtful; yet they occur frequently, making it difficult for patients to work out their problems in peace.

Less gross, but nonetheless disconcerting, may be the solicitous inquiries of respectful and interested friends. "How are things going? What are you getting out of it? Is it proving worth while?" are legitimate questions for a patient to ask himself at various points along the road, and again at the end of the way. But an outsider has no way of gauging into what distressing phase of the analysis his question may fall. Nor can he be aware of the impossibility of answering such a question, except by reassuring generalities or evasions. The wise patient is rarely willing to divulge to his well-meaning friends the intimate personal difficulties which can profitably be shared only with the psychoanalyst; because to pour out his heart to his friends will only impede the progress of his treatment.

Sometimes, however, the patient himself draws this little world of interested and curious spectators into the vortex of the analysis. Patients go through phases in which consciously or unconsciously they want to sabotage their analyses. At such times a patient may build up two groups of allies: on one side those who support the analysis; and on the other those who are hostile to it. According to his mood, he associates now with one circle and now with the other; and within the span of a single day he may unwittingly give to members of each group wholly opposite accounts of what is going on in the analysis, thus leading them to respond with conflicting counsel.

This may begin with the first analytic session. A patient who had come to analysis eagerly and yet with deep reluctance, resolved to tell no one about it. Nevertheless, she left her first session to make an unpremeditated call on a relative in whose presence she made a slip of the tongue which betrayed the fact that she had begun an analysis. This relative was the person who was most influential in the patient's life, and most certain to oppose the analysis bitterly.

Such episodes are likely to happen in each recurring period of difficulty in the course of any analysis. It is an exceptional and fortunate patient whose friends and relatives refuse to allow themselves to be drawn into the struggle, and who say to the patient, "Keep your confidences for your analysis, and work out your problems there."

The Patient's Need for Periods of Isolation

The reasons for the patient's need for periods of isolation from his family and friends may be summarized as follows: (1) Frequently these relationships have been invested with all the neurotic problems of the patient. (2) Often they are used as a target for his symptomatic behavior. (3) These symptoms and difficulties will frequently become exaggerated whenever the patient is among his old friends. (4) On the other hand, patients may also use friends and relatives in order to cover and escape from the difficulties which the analyst is trying to make them face. (5) Friends and relatives may have an over-solicitous concern for the patient's welfare and, since they know him well, they may be sensitive to every mood swing which occurs as the patient works through difficult phases of his treatment. This in turn may be hard both on the patient and on them. Therefore, it often is an act of kindness to the family and to intimate friends to give them a respite from their responsibilities and from continual contact with the patient, since such a respite may both shorten the treatment and spare everyone distress. (6) Often it would permanently damage the relationship if either the patient or the analyst were to tell friends or relatives of the fear, envy, hostility and suspicion which the patient may have harbored in secret, and which the analysis is aiming to eliminate. Therefore, the analyst can rarely be wholly frank and open with the patient's friends or relatives and they are likely to sense his reservations and evasions, and to resent them. They will think him either indirect, or a boor. (7) On the other hand, when friends have been badly used by the patient because of his neurosis, the justifiable resentments which they have sedulously held in check for years are likely to come out just when the patient is beginning to shed his neurotic attitudes toward them. The long pent-up resentments are frequently ventilated at this point either against the patient or against the analysis, or both. Therefore, it may be necessary to shield the patient from these pent-up feelings until he is well on the way to recovery.

From time to time, all of these considerations, as well as those mentioned in Chapter XI make it wise for the analysis to serve as a buffer, dividing the patient temporarily from his usual associates. When this happens, however, unless it will excite in the patient a dangerous amount of distrust and jealousy, the analyst must be ready to satisfy the misgivings of responsible members of the family and to allay their anxieties as much as he can. Where, because of the patient's attitude, it is not safe for him to approach the family or friends directly, he must make this point clear to them through the family physician or through some trusted intermediary. It is best if the patient can see the wisdom and fairness of allowing the analyst to make his own explanations to those who would otherwise be hurt or mystified; but early in a treatment it is rarely possible to do this.

For his part, the conscientious and considerate analyst ought never to forget that both by the very nature of his work and because he must often hold the family at arm's length, he puts a great strain on all of those who love the patient and who are anxious about him. The analyst does not relish his role; yet, there are times when in the interest of his patient he is forced for a time to ride roughshod over the feelings of a family. Since his therapeutic responsibility to the patient must come first, when this becomes necessary, all he can do is to ask the family to have patience until he has reached a point in the analysis when it will be possible for him to talk to them freely without endangering the treatment.

Sometimes such a talk can safely take place only in the presence of the patient himself. In all of these matters, however, there are no absolute rules. The reason for mentioning them here is to emphasize to patients, to the families of prospective patients, and to their physicians that there are times when the analyst is forced to put their feelings to one side, lest he jeopardize his therapeutic leverage with the patient.

Chapter XIII

THE RELATIONSHIP OF THE REFERRING PHYSICIAN TO THE ANALYSIS

The Referral

The selection of patients for analytic treatment is based partly on technical aspects of the patient's illness and personality, and partly on practical considerations, many of which cannot be evaluated accurately ahead of time. Consequently it usually is wise to begin an analysis tentatively, deferring for some weeks the final decision as to its wisdom. Patients are advised, therefore, to consider the first weeks or months as a trial period, during the course of which the patient and the analyst will decide together on the advisability of continuing the analysis. It is for this reason that psychoanalytic clinics assign their most experienced leaders to the task of selecting patients.

It is essential that the general physician should be equally cautious when urging a patient to consider analysis. When an internist refers a patient to some other medical specialist, he does not attempt to dictate what treatment that specialist will employ. He does not usually refer a patient to a surgeon for operation, but rather for an opinion as to the advisability of operating, the kind of operation, if any, its timing, etc. The same procedure should govern the referral of patients to psychoanalysis. It is well not to refer a patient to a psychoanalyst "for analysis", but rather for consultation as to the desirability of an analysis. Once a definite opinion has been secured as to the advisability of this step, the effort to persuade the patient to go ahead can be undertaken without further hesitation. Otherwise the analyst may find himself facing a patient who has been persuaded by his physician that analysis is his one hope for health, when that patient may have an illness no sensible analyst would attempt to analyze.

The Family Physician During the Course of the Analysis

(a) *Discretion*

During the course of the analysis the referring physician can rarely be taken fully into the analyst's confidence. In many instances patients themselves are explicit in their requests that nothing of what they tell the analyst should be communicated to their physicians. This can create an awkward situation for the psychoanalyst; but unless the patient is psychotic or otherwise irresponsible, the analyst's responsibility to the patient must take precedence over his desire to be courteous to his medical colleague. In the course of the analysis, however, it may become clear that the patient's request arose from a neurotic distortion of his attitude towards the family physician. When this is the case, and when this aspect of the neurosis has been resolved, the patient will withdraw his request, leaving the psychoanalyst free, within reason, to take the referring physician into his confidence.

Certainly a patient's reluctance to have his story passed on to anyone other than the analyst is never entirely neurotic. To expect a patient to unburden himself without reserve in the presence of anyone is asking a great deal. To expect him to do this before two people may be asking the impossible. Yet that is what it would amount to if a psychoanalyst said to his patient not, "What you say here is for my ears alone", but "What you say here is for my ears and those of your family physician." The patient's confident sense of privacy cannot be violated in this way without seriously jeopardizing his ability to be completely frank.

At the same time the analyst must always keep in mind the fact that it is wholly natural and legitimate for the family physician to have a personal interest in and sense of responsibility for his patient, as well as a scientific interest in the progress of the analysis and a reasonable amount of sheer curiosity to boot. Nevertheless, even when the patient makes no specific request to the analyst not to discuss his material with his physician, the physician's interest or curiosity can be gratified only sparingly and in general terms during the course of the analysis. In the long run, such discretion is advantageous to the physician himself. During the course of an analysis, patients sometimes act out a great deal of rage on their friends, families, and medical advisers, as well as on their analysts. Therefore, it may actually protect the post-analytic relationship of the doctor to his patient if the physician does not become too intimately involved in the analysis. Furthermore, this policy can protect the relationship of the physician to the patient's family. In the course of any difficult treatment, the family often attempts to learn more about the patient than is wise for them to know at the time. They may bring heavy pressure to bear on the physician to make unwise disclosures. Lack of detailed information will be his best protection in this situation, since to know yet to withhold details might seriously jeopardize his relationship to the whole family. If the physician says to the family, "I have confidence in the analyst, and I do not ask him to violate his patient's confidence," he both protects himself and sets them a good example.

When, for any reason, the analyst feels that he must take the family physician into his confidence, the latter should feel obligated never to divulge such confidence to anyone. Even when a trivial fact is involved, it may be fatal to an analysis if it leaks out via the physician to family or friends and thence ultimately back again to the patient. The particular item may be something which the patient himself may be ready to tell anyone; but the fact that it escaped the analytic chamber means to the patient that more important things can also leak. Therefore, the temptation to minor indiscretions must be resisted constantly. It is impossible to exaggerate the importance of this warning. The path may be tortuous, but it ultimately leads back to the patient with a fated precision. As an actual example: from the psychoanalyst to the thoroughly trusted physician of the family; from this physician, out of the goodness of his heart, to comfort the anxious mother; from the mother, because of her natural need for reassurance, to her "best friend"; from the "best friend" to her own daughter "as a warning"; from the daughter to her husband; from him to the patient's husband; thence to the patient; and from the patient back to the psychoanalyst. With the best of will, families and friends can be guilty of this kind of indiscretion, not out of malice but either out of sympathy or the pressure of their own needs. Therefore, the analyst must observe a code that makes of him a safe-deposit box to which the patient alone holds the key. Only in this way can the patient feel that the analyst is the sole repository of his confidences. This is not mysterious psycho-analytic cultism. It is a policy which has been forced upon analysts by their experiences in dealing with doctors, friends, and relatives of patients; and it applies just as much to fel-low-analysts as to anyone else. Of all physicians, the psychoanalyst has the least right to talk about his patients, even to his colleagues, without protecting meticulously the identities of these patients. A good analyst is always close-mouthed.

(b) *The Problem of Divided Loyalties*

In many other ways the analyst and the general physician must have a clear understanding if they are not to impede the patient's progress.

Not only do patients become attached to their physicians; physicians also become attached to their patients. And even after deciding to refer a patient for analysis, some physicians find it difficult to turn the patient over to a new adviser. The greater the effort the physician has made and the more he has played the role of a trusted counsellor and friend, the more difficult it may be for him to relinquish his role to the analyst.

That this might cost anyone a pang of jealousy is only

human and natural; nevertheless, the transition is usually handled with generosity. Occasionally, however, it makes serious trouble. It may lead the physician to hang on to a patient for years longer than he should, trying to cure the patient himself. Or after finally bringing himself to give up the patient, the physician may find it so intolerable that his patient now confides in someone else that he may interfere in many ways. He may try repeatedly to learn what is going on, or he may try to anticipate everything the patient will say, making light of it, prejudging what is important, directing the patient what to tell the analyst; and most disrupting of all, he may make the patient feel that not to confide first in him is an act of disloyalty. This may end with the patient using the family doctor as a spillway through which to pour out much of the material which should be brought to the analysis.

Not long ago two young women were referred to an analyst by two well-known physicians. To an amazing extent their neuroses were identical. They came from similar backgrounds. The pattern of their early lives had been remarkably alike. They had made rather similar marriages to men with not dissimilar problems; and they had developed almost identical neurotic symptoms and personality distortions.

There, however, the parallel ceased. One young woman had been brought to analysis at the age of twenty-three, within four months of the onset of outspoken symptoms. Furthermore, her doctor, who pretended to no knowledge of psychiatry, said to the analyst in the presence of the patient: "I am very fond of this young lady, and she of me. I have known her and taken care of her for many years. I have been her father confessor. It isn't going to be easy for her to talk to someone else; and it will be impossible if at the same time she goes on talking to me. If she does that, all you will get will be warmed-over material. Everything will be predigested with me; and you'll never get anywhere. Therefore at this point I am going to retire from the picture. I have told my assistant to take care of all routine medical problems, and to call me only in case of something special. I'll miss my young friend; but this is the best contribution I can make to her recovery." This wise and generous physician had the satisfaction of seeing his patient complete her analysis successfully in a remarkably short time.

The other physician prided himself on his knowledge of psychiatry and on his own personal brand of psychotherapy. He sent the patient to analysis when she was in her mid-thirties, after he had spent over twelve years in ineffectual efforts to treat her himself. He actually told the analyst that he was sending the patient to him to get rid of her. Nevertheless, he could not give her up. He continued to see her almost daily, often on her way to her analytic session. He encouraged or permitted her to indulge in long talks with him, so that by the time she came to her analytic hour, her need to confide in anyone had spent itself, and she could say little or nothing to the analyst. She even held back a great deal of vital information because she had the feeling that she had already discussed it fully with her physician, and because this daily contact with her physician held her in a constant struggle between conflicting loyalties. Naturally this patient made no progress.

For a long time the analyst did not even know that all this was going on. When it finally was acknowledged, he recognized the neurotic basis of the physician's behavior and how it fitted into and fed the pattern of the patient's neurosis, and he set himself to break up the relationship. Nevertheless, it took two years of completely frustrated pseudo-analysis before he was able to wean the patient away from her neurotic dependence on her doctor; and he could do this only by backing out of the picture himself and by insisting that she make a fresh start with another analyst and a new medical adviser. Only then did her analysis really start. This is an extreme example; but it happens in lesser degrees in many analyses.

Nevertheless, the analyst should be reasonably generous and tolerant towards his non-analytic colleagues, even when they make trouble for him and his patients. If he himself has ever had to sit beside the analysis of some well-loved friend or relative, he will know how hard it can be to keep one's hands off. This experience should help him to understand and sympathize with the position of his medical colleagues and of the families of his patients. When dealing with his own patients, the analyst is able to maintain a high degree of tolerance for their difficulties, and to accept erratic or even dangerous behavior with considerable peace of mind. This is possible for him because he is not deeply involved emotionally, and because he does not live with his patients and their symptoms twenty-four hours a day, and finally because he knows and understands what is going on. The patient's ups and downs make sense to him. But when this same analyst sits in relative ignorance beside the analysis of some member of his own family, he will for the first time experience the difficulty of this position.

(c) *Physical Care During Analysis*

Throughout an analysis a patient must be guarded against the occurrence of physical illness. Rarely, if ever, will the psychoanalyst attempt to perform this function himself, lest it interfere with his value as a psychoanalyst. Instead, at any hint of physical disturbance he will expect the patient to turn to his usual medical adviser. This necessitates a good working understanding between the two, something which will be hard to achieve if the general physician happens to be one who is hostile to psychoanalysis. Should this make an understanding impossible, it may become necessary for the psychoanalyst to insist that the patient turn to another medical adviser for the duration of the analytic treatment. Nowadays, however, such disagreements are rare, and whenever a question arises as to the organic or psychogenic or mixed nature of any physical disturbance which occurs during an analysis, the two physicians must be able to confer without the usual reserves if they are to reach a point of view which does justice to all possibilities. Unresolved difficulties will only perplex the patient, and not help him.

If a patient seeks a new physical examination at every moment of panic, or if he is one of those who retreat into real or feigned illness whenever the going becomes difficult, then some constructive method of handling this tendency must be agreed upon. Otherwise, to his own ultimate damage, the patient will play off the internist against the analyst, and vice versa. If it becomes clear that the constant tendency to resort to medical help does not arise out of physical disabilities which threaten the patient's fundamental health, it may become necessary for a limited time to forbid the patient to seek medical advice of any kind without the analyst's consent. Before this is done, however, the sanction and support of the medical adviser should be secured.

The opposite tendency may also be encountered. Some patients refuse to face the reality of organic illness, minimizing or hiding serious and even painful symptoms, giving evasive and conflicting descriptions of them, and resisting the pressure of their families or of the analyst to seek medical advice. Thus a patient with active tuberculosis refused for a time to take his temperature, to limit his activities, or to consult his physician. When such an impasse persists, it may force an interruption of the analysis, unless it has been possible to eliminate through the analysis the patient's objection to accepting medical help.

The relation of physical illness to emotional processes is far more complex than this brief note might suggest, and is connected with many scientific problems not directly related to these practical issues. These problems must also be considered in connection with the vexed question of whether nonmedical analysts should be allowed to do therapeutic analyses. This issue is discussed in Chapter XXIII.

Chapter XIV

THE APPROACH TO PSYCHOANALYSIS

In a sense it is natural that people turn to psychoanalysis as a last resort. As we pointed out in Chapter IV, simple remedies for psychological difficulties should be tried until they prove ineffectual. At the same time, one should keep in mind the warning given in that chapter against persisting in such efforts too long. Many years can be lost in heroic but futile and heartbreaking efforts at self-help or compromise; and the psychoanalyst could often save these years by predicting with fair accuracy when these simple methods have a reasonable chance to succeed. In the early stage of a neurosis, however, the analyst is able only rarely to persuade a prospective patient, and his family and his physician to accept his judgment. This is because turning to analysis for help presupposes an acknowledgment of illness and of an inability to help oneself, which people usually consider to be a sign of weakness. Actually this step requires wisdom, humility, honesty, and courage.

For lack of this, patients regularly come to analysis much later than they should, and their histories almost uniformly tell of a lifetime of ineffectual efforts to solve internal problems by external changes. Childhood problems were dealt with by changes in disciplinary regime. Difficulties in school were met by transferring to another school; or treatment was postponed while waiting to see if the symptoms would disappear with the shift from elementary school to high school, from day school to boarding school, from school to college. In college it was expected that things would improve after graduation. Then the solution was sought in a job, in changing jobs, or in marriage, and in having first one child and then several, or finally in divorces and new marriages.

Ultimately, however, every adult reaches a point at which there are no further significant changes left to make in the outer forms of his life. At this point an intensification of persisting neurotic symptoms occurs, complicated now by depression and anxiety; and it is this which forces the average man to consider analysis, perhaps for the first time. He might have saved himself many years of suffering and of frustration if, long before, he had had the humility and foresight to acknowledge that his illness was within himself. It is rare for external changes to result in significant psychological readjustments, because our internal problems usually follow us into new settings. Only when for special reasons the external change produces internal changes can it initiate lasting improvements.

The Tendency to Postpone Psychotherapy

There are two causes for the universal tendency to postpone treatment. To one we have already alluded—namely, the feeling of shame and guilt which attaches to psychological illness (cf. Chapters II and III). This is only partly cultural in origin; but to this extent it can be modified by the processes of education, which are slowly producing a more enlightened attitude in people in general. This change is apparent already. Today, in many schools and colleges, psychotherapy is made available to youngsters who are in trouble; and in centers for the treatment of neuroses (such as the Austen Riggs Foundation in Stockbridge, Massachusetts) to an increasing degree the patients are in their college years.

The other cause of delayed treatment is more difficult to alter. It arises out of the fact that the neurotic process does not always hurt the patient himself. Sometimes it is chiefly his family and friends who suffer. Usually both effects occur in varying proportions. Certain symptoms, however, cause overwhelming pain to the patient, such as depression or anxiety, humiliating feelings of inadequacy, or thoughts and acts which patients themselves look upon as foolish but which they are compelled to do in spite of themselves. Naturally every patient wants to get rid of such symptoms as these. Yet, out of pride he will hide them as long as possible, struggling alone as best he can to shed his painful symptoms, until failure finally forces him to give in and ask for help.

The existence of another group of symptoms, which hurt the patient little if at all, is one of the special peculiarities of the neurotic process. Among these symptoms are the neurotic elements in our personalities. They may make us work too hard, eat too much, play too hard, compete too violently. Or they may turn us into spectators rather than participants in life, philosophers or critics rather than doers. They can produce misanthropes or philanthropists. If we are gifted we can even turn these neurotic weaknesses into self-gratifying or socially acceptable activities. Although families and associates pay a high price for them, they cause little immediate suffering to the patient himself, certainly nothing compared to the gratifications which they bring. Therefore we tend to pride ourselves on such quirks as these, and to defend them against interference, however therapeutic.

Thus the spur which drives man to seek help is usually his own suffering. Illnesses which do not hurt the patient himself are usually neglected, often until it is too late. Nowhere does this apply more than in psychiatry. I cannot make anyone else suffer the pain of my broken leg, as I inevitably make others suffer through my neurosis. This is especially clear when the family of a patient allows itself to be ruled by the patient's symptoms. Thus a woman with a phobia of the country forced her family to spend their vacations in town. A man with a fear of heights made his family live on the ground floor. A woman with a neurotic hostility to people, which took the form of acute anxiety in social gatherings, isolated her husband and children from all normal social life. A compulsive gambler put his family through repeated stretches of poverty. In each of these cases, it would have precipitated even more violent neurotic symptoms and much domestic warfare if the families had refused to submit to the tyranny of these symptoms. The patients themselves would either have cracked up, or they would have come to treatment years earlier. Thus tender and loving patience, if misapplied, can actually block the road to health. As Macfie Campbell once said, a family is a dictatorship ruled by its sickest member; and a patient's chance of health may depend ultimately upon the steadfastness of his family in refusing to accept servitude to his illness. It is a sound principle that every patient must pay the price of his own neurotic incapacity. If the family pays these debts for him, then he will suffer little pain; and there will be nothing to spur him on towards treatment.

Not infrequently a patient seems to feel that the only trait which prevents his being a nonentity is his neurosis. Sometimes this protest is quite frank: "I want to get well, but I don't want to change," or, "If I am analyzed, I will turn out just like everyone else," or "I'll lose my ability to write or paint." It is as though, stripped of their neurotic eccentricities, people would lose all individuality and creative capacity. Actually once freed of neurotic insecurity, human beings become more productive and less timid and conformist than before. Freedom from neurosis lessens the compulsive striving for pseudo-originality for its own sake; yet no one is as conformist as the child, except perhaps the secret child that is hidden in every adult.

The prospective patient realizes none of these simple facts. He wants to blame situations, illness, disappointments, or other people for his neurosis, i.e., everything and anything but his own personality. Therefore, his personality as such is the last thing he wants the analyst to meddle with. Yet, as we have pointed out (Chapter IV), basic therapy requires a profound personality alteration, not unlike that which sometimes occurs in the course of a deep and sincere religious conversion. It is the protest that we do not want to change and our proud and stiff-necked determination not to let any analyst "meddle with" our personalities, which causes the longest delays of all in seeking psychiatric treatment, even when this is desperately needed.

The Reluctant Patient

In varying degrees, then, every patient is reluctant; and it is hard to stand aside and watch someone heading for avoidable disaster, especially when it is his pride or ignorance which makes him unwilling to accept help. Consequently, the patient's family or physician is sometimes tempted to beg, cajole or bribe the patient into analysis. However well intended this may be, it usually is futile. The analyst can do little for the patient who comes actually against his will. He can hold up a mirror to the patient in an effort to induce him to look honestly at his life, his personality, and his neurotic incapacities. He can hold out legitimate expectations of relief through long, hard analytical work. He can try to induce the family to remove all the devices with which they have been protecting the patient from paying the price of his own illness. Sometimes the analyst may even induce the patient to try some form of preliminary psychotherapy, short of analysis. For the reluctant patient these efforts constitute the only effective ante-chamber to psychoanalysis.

In the end, however, the patient who comes merely to please someone else, confronts the analyst with a difficult problem. If the psychoanalyst paints an honest picture of the time and effort which treatment will entail, the patient will almost certainly run away. True, he may return years later; but to the extent to which this has cost the patient additional years of illness, it is a therapeutic defeat.

If, on the other hand, the psychoanalyst minimizes the difficulties and duration of treatment and plays for a warm and friendly contact, he may succeed in luring the patient into analysis. Furthermore, the patient may even improve for a time; but this lack of any sense of illness and the absence of a serious therapeutic purpose will usually lead him to break off as soon as the painful phases of the treatment begin. Such a patient usually goes off bitterly convinced that he has tried psychoanalysis and that it has failed. Therefore, even when it may seem callous it usually is wise to send the reluctant patient away to wait until his increasing disabilities force him to return, this time with a conscious need and purpose that will carry him through the treatment. The one important exception to this is in adolescence. The youngster who is resentful, resistant, and uncomprehending, may remain in treatment notwithstanding. He does this at first, not out of any understanding of his illness, nor because of any clear therapeutic purpose, but because he needs so desperately the substitute parent which the analyst represents. He needs the analyst as an ally against his own parents and against his own conflict-laden moods; and the analyst in turn can utilize this desperate need to help the adolescent mature.

Psychoanalysis as a Preventive Measure

The growth of the general cultural influence of psychoanalysis has coincided with the development of the mental hygiene movement, and with an increasing emphasis on preventive medicine in general. Before the introduction of psychoanalysis, the therapy of the neuroses was largely palliative, employing methods which even in ancient Greece had succeeded in making the lives of patients more comfortable (cf. Chapter IV). Psychoanalytic technique makes it possible for the first time to investigate and alter the complex psychological roots of neuroses.

Therapeutic triumphs led naturally to attempts to use psychoanalysis as a preventive measure. In the first place, psychoanalysis frequently makes it possible to recognize incipient phases of illness, before either the patient or his family has become aware of the gravity or the imminence of danger. Secondly, serious mental illnesses sometimes start quite insidiously in seemingly mild neurotic disturbances; and in some of these cases the advance of the illness can be checked by using analytic methods early, before the pathological process has had time to become irreversible.

Yet this very ability to foresee future difficulties may place the psychoanalyst in a difficult position. The old-fashioned psychiatrist played a simple role, because he dealt almost exclusively with fully developed mental diseases. No effort was made to diagnose the process of illness until it was sufficiently advanced to be obvious even to the layman. Therefore, when the psychiatrist said to the family, "This is a sick man who must be hospitalized," no one could accuse the doctor of being an alarmist, or of looking at everything from a psychiatric bias, or of being mercenary.

The psychoanalyst on the other hand frequently has to give people warnings which they do not want to hear. He may have to tell a family that a relative who seems fairly normal to them is really quite ill, and that he should go to an analyst in order to try to prevent the further development of this sickness. Then if the analysis succeeds and illness does not follow, there will always be some who doubt that it would ever have developed anyhow. Only rarely is it possible to prove that without treatment the alarming prophesy would have materialized. On the other hand if the treatment fails and illness supervenes, the analyst is quite likely to be accused of having caused the very illness which he was trying to prevent. Thus whatever happens, there will be more than one friend and relative who will think that the patient has been misled into undertaking unwise or at least unnecessary treatment.

Under these circumstances the psychoanalyst must expect and even invite frank skepticism from the friends and relatives of a prospective patient. To resent this would be to expect to be looked upon as omniscient. Indeed, when the responsible friends and relatives express all their doubts frankly to the psychoanalyst ahead of time the analyst has a chance to deal with these doubts before they can cause trouble. He can then establish a relationship of confidence, which will protect the subsequent course of the analysis. Furthermore, the relative who from time to time is free to blow off steam to the analyst, or to some representative of the analyst, is less likely to sabotage the analysis directly with the patient.

Even where all misgivings are handled openly, however, the symptoms which the patient reveals to the analyst may have to remain hidden from the rest of the world. It might, for instance, do irreparable damage to reveal a sexual perversion which a patient has hidden, and for which he now seeks help. Therefore, when the patient is neither a child nor so ill as to be irresponsible, it is the psychoanalyst's duty to protect the patient's confidence by indicating to his interested relatives and physician only that there are serious symptoms which he does not feel free to discuss with anyone. Such evasiveness, however conscientious, cannot fail to arouse some measure of distrust.

Where this distrust cannot be overcome, as, for instance, when dealing with a neurotic family, or with a family that has had its confidence shaken by previous incompetent or dishonest advice, it may be possible for the analyst to allay such distrust only by refusing to accept the patient for treatment himself, insisting instead on sending the patient to a carefully chosen colleague. This can, at least, eliminate the suspicion that the psychoanalyst's judgment is influenced by mercenary considerations.

The basic solution of this problem lies, however, not in such devices, but in the growth of confidence in psychoanalytic integrity and judgment; and this in turn will come only as psychoanalytic judgment itself improves, and as the general public learns to deal only with those who are qualified to practice by the long and thorough training described in Chapter XXII.

There is another form in which the problem of preventive

analysis may present itself to the psychoanalyst. His advice may be sought by a patient who comes with an intrinsically mild neurotic disturbance, a complaint which might yield quickly to almost any kind of sensible and superficial help. Behind the specific symptom, however, the analyst may detect the signs of a more profound process. The decision must then be made whether it is better to try to cure the symptom directly, since this is the burden of the patient's major complaint, or to use it as a lead to underlying difficulties.

Sometimes curing a symptom only obscures a disease process, which will reappear with the next strain. This is comparable to the danger of masking the painful symptoms of an acute surgical emergency by a too free use of morphine. Only the opportunist in psychiatry will choose such a course. Yet when an analyst uses a patient's symptom to direct the patient's attention to underlying problems, the patient will soon feel worse instead of better, whereupon the patient and the family may become indignant and alarmed, not realizing that this painful facing of hidden illness is essential as a first step towards health. If the patient has been properly forewarned, and if his capacity to stand the rigors of treatment has been gauged accurately, the ultimate results will justify these growing pains. Yet to accept with unshaken trust an increase in the pain from which one is seeking relief demands an almost blind faith; and it is not surprising that patients and families rebel. Here again the only ultimate safeguard for the layman is the adequacy of the psychoanalyst's training.

The Use of Psychoanalysis as a Preventive Measure in Childhood

The war taught us that the only way to prevent the full development of the neurotic state is by intensive treatment of the neurotic process as soon as its presence can be recognized. Therefore, the best time to prevent neuroses is in the early years of life. Let us recapitulate here what was pointed out in Chapter III: (a) It is inherent in the very nature of the growth process of the human being to have inner psychic conflicts in infancy and childhood. (b) Because of our ability to use symbolic thinking, we represent these conflicts symbolically in thought and action, and in their emotional concomitants. (c) Finally, we render much of this conflict unconscious, with the consequence that the symbols of the conflict become detached from their original psychological sources to initiate what we call "the neurotic process." With the recognition of these basic facts, the various elements in a program of prevention become clear.

First, we would test the effects of different forms of social and family structure on the tendency to deal with conflicts by repression. Second, we would try to educate young parents in the methods by which the tendency of children to repress can be minimized. Finally we would treat every neurotic upset of childhood as an acute medical emergency, which demanded immediate and intensive analytic help. The purpose of this would be to bring into the full light of consciousness the unconscious conflicts out of which those early neurotic episodes arose, so that they would not leave behind them those residual unconscious forces which distort the later adult personality. This is the theoretical basis for child analysis; which may ultimately prove to be one of the greatest contributions of psychoanalysis to human progress.

Certainly the ancient technique of disciplining a child out of his symptoms has proved to be as destructive as the naively optimistic hope that left to himself the child outgrows his difficulties. At best, these devices merely bury the symptoms, while allowing the underlying unconscious roots to persist. Furthermore, it is one of the deeply disappointing facts of human life that children even from happy families often develop serious neurotic problems. Evidently there are limits both to the preventive virtues and to the healing powers of family happiness as we know it today. Why this

is true, and what to do about it constitute one of the great
cultural challenges of our times.

When Should Analysis be Attempted?

How early in the development of a neurosis should analysis
be undertaken? Let us consider a few examples. Take for
instance a frequent problem, that of a spinster in her early
thirties. She has never been happy in her social relationships. Whether idle or active, she has manifested veiled
emotional and neurotic disturbances for years, but has always
been able to run away from them. She has escaped from
them into work. She has gone on vacations abroad and at
home. She has tried shifting from one social group
to another. She has turned successively to Christian Science,
social work, theosophy and art. Yet as the years have gone
on, for reasons which she cannot explain, frustration and
defeat have followed her, until suddenly she is confronted by
one of the specters that she has always dreaded most, i.e.
the fear of becoming an old maid. By this time, however,
her fear is complicated by reality; because she has reached
an age at which most of the men she knows are already married. Indeed many are husbands of her friends, which infects
her limited social life with a secret rage and envy. Other
men have remained unmarried for their own neurotic reasons.
Therefore, as she reaches out blindly for inappropriate men,
she suffers repeated disappointments. Finally some particularly disappointing episode becomes too much to bear and
precipitates her into a "nervous breakdown," i.e., into a fully-
developed emotional or mental disturbance.

The further course of such a patient reveals another significant fact, namely that the fight is not won even when the
patient recovers from this acute upset. She emerges from her
illness to face the same external realities and the same inner
psychological mechanisms, until and unless analysis frees her
from them. Yet, even the patient who has been cured

of a neurosis at this late date, may be like a prisoner emerging from a long prison sentence. No magic can restore the lost years, nor make the road ahead an easy one.

When should such a patient have been analyzed? There would have been an opportunity in childhood, when she first manifested temper-tantrums, night terrors, a retreat into books or other work, an avoidance of contemporaries, and an excessive dependency upon adults. There would have been an opportunity in adolescence when the patient had a short but serious emotional upset on going away to camp for the first time (euphemistically called "home-sickness"). There would have been an opportunity in her early twenties when the patient's social uneasiness, her lost attitude in the world, and her excessive emotional swings became unmistakable. Sometimes these opportunities are missed because of the false pride of families who refuse to recognize the existence of a neurosis. Sometimes they are missed because the patient herself is proud and defiant, or secretive and ashamed, and rejects every effort to lead her to help. Whatever the cause of the delay, its ultimate effects on the patient's life are tragic.

Comparable to such a case is the fate of the bachelor who comes to the analyst at a similar age. He has been disappointed in his emotional relationships and in his work-life. He has met defeat because neurotic obstacles within himself have stood between him and success. Here again, even after successful analytic treatment, the patient comes out of the prison of his illness to face a world in which opportunities for further training and for employment may be seriously curtailed. His bungling progress through school or college or professional school, or through the early years of a business or professional career, has marred his record, so that the latter does not do justice to his potential abilities. This in itself limits his future opportunities. Therefore, even if he achieves freedom from his neurosis, he faces a difficult task. Sometimes he must turn back to train himself for competition with people twenty years his junior. Sometimes he must abandon one field of work for another. These difficult readjustments are the inevitable consequences of years of neglected neuroses, and for lost years, analysis has no magical assuagement. It cannot turn back the hands of the clock.

Therefore, one asks when had analysis best be applied? In the early years, when the transient neurotic outbursts of childhood gave warning of possible future difficulties? In adolescence? Or at the recurrence of difficulties in the twenties? The specific time can be chosen only in terms of the needs of each patient; but the general principle holds that "the earlier the better", both because the fresh neurosis is less resistant to therapy, and because early treatment can save many years of tragic waste and frustration.

These are some of the considerations which make one recommend that treatment be instituted just as early as the patient can be brought to realize his need of help. It is rarely wise to wait long to see if a patient won't "outgrow it", or, on the other hand, to protect a patient to a point at which it becomes easier for him to live with his neurosis than to face the rigors of treatment. Whether as therapy or as prevention, psychoanalysis can function effectively only for someone who has become convinced of the necessity of the step he is taking, who is ready to face his neurotic tendencies, who has abandoned the effort to blame his maladjustments on physical illness, external circumstances or other people, and who comes willingly and largely on his own initiative. In many cases, and especially in the effort to prevent the development of illness before it is fully manifest, the analyst's first task is to prepare the patient for treatment by bringing him to this fully cooperative viewpoint. This ante-chamber to analysis may sometimes take a long time.

6. *Who Can Be Analyzed?*

(a) *Intelligence*

Often one is asked whether formal education and intelligence are essential for an analysis. This is not a matter about which one may be dogmatic. It is clear that, in general, a fine intelligence is an asset but that formal education matters little. There have been efforts to use psychoanalytic methods to study primitive savages, simple people in our own society, and the mentally defective, and in the latter case to alter their sudden emotional tantrums. The immediate therapeutic value of these studies is less certain than is their scientific interest.

(b) *Age Limits*

Are there age-limits outside of which analysis is impossible? Certain special technical problems arise in the psychoanalytic investigation of infants before they have reached the age of spoken language. Technically, it comes down to the question of how far gestures, play, direct emotional expression and the like can be used as a substitute for the spoken word in tracing the patterns of free associations to reach an understanding of the pre-verbal process by which the infant or child learns to represent symbolically the conflicts which he represses. Much important research centers about this problem, but some results have already been achieved which are theoretically illuminating and therapeutically gratifying.

With older children no such technical difficulties exist. In this age-period the exploration of unconscious influences and their conscious resolution is an important phase of current psychoanalytic development. In adolescence, the main obstacle to successful work is the patient's temptation to blame his difficulties on the vicissitudes of home, school and college, and to reject all personal responsibility for the task of getting well. Sometimes this may be so difficult to overcome that the youth must be allowed to flounder until he becomes convinced of his need. This is dangerous, however; and whenever the adolescent neurosis contains any premonitions of delinquency or severe mental illness, one dares not wait for the patient's awareness of his own illness to develop. By that time it may be too late for help (v.s. Section 4).

Old age, too, brings its perplexities. Beyond a certain age one would hesitate to recommend a form of treatment which in the present state of our knowledge must last so long. What that "certain age" is, however, must be determined for every patient individually. What one person can no longer undertake profitably at forty-five, another can carry through at fifty-five or sixty. Many considerations will enter into that decision: the duration of the neurotic difficulties; the patient's earlier flexibility and health in meeting the challenges of life; the social, familial, and economic problems which the patient has to face, etc. The decision will rest on grounds of practical common sense, as well as on technical issues, and must be thoroughly discussed between the psychoanalyst and the patient or his family before treatment is undertaken.

Chapter XV

JUDGING THE COURSE AND OUTCOME OF
AN ANALYSIS

That many analyses fail to achieve complete success goes without saying. To anticipate the same measure of therapy in so heterogeneous a lot of illnesses as those which are brought to the psychoanalyst is to expect something that no other medical therapy can claim, namely the ability to treat all illnesses with equal effectiveness. It is often forgotten that, under the cover of some such euphemistic term as a "nervous breakdown", the psychoanalyst faces many diverse problems, e.g., drug addictions, the perversions, every known form of psychoneurosis, psychopathic personalities, delinquency, incipient insanities of various kinds, etc. One does not expect surgery to achieve the same results in cancer, a brain tumor, appendicitis, and a boil. We estimate the value of surgery separately in terms of each disease entity which it attempts to help. In the same way the therapeutic value of psychoanalysis must be judged separately for each of the conditions which it attempts to treat.

The Data Which Are Essential for Judging

To judge accurately either the progress or the outcome of a psychoanalytic treatment requires exceptional patience and caution. This is because it is difficult for an outsider to know the essential facts without which no judgment can be valid. Some of these facts are obvious, e.g.: (1) Was the patient analyzed by a competent and properly trained psychoanalyst? (2) Was the analysis approximately completed, or prematurely interrupted by circumstances over which neither the patient nor the analyst had any control? (3) What were the symptoms and difficulties which brought the patient to the psychoanalyst for treatment, and what would be the normal outcome of such a condition if untreated? (4) What would be the expected course and outcome of the psychoanalytic treatment of such a case? (a) under favorable circumstances, (b) under unfavorable circumstances? (5) What especially favorable or unfavorable influences affected the progress of this particular analysis? (6) Finally, what was the condition of the patient at the end of the treatment in comparison (a) with his condition when he began, (b) with the best that might be hoped for?

Many considerations in addition to these are often important; but with this minimal information on hand, competent opinion would usually be possible. Unfortunately these data are rarely accessible, even to interested friends and relatives. No other patients are equally reticent about their symptoms, and nowhere else would the least abuse of professional confidence have such disastrous effects upon the treatment itself. As a result, the psychoanalyst frequently must accept criticisms which are unfounded, without being free to say a word in defense or explanation. As we have pointed out, it is sometimes impossible for the analyst to take anyone into his confidence, not even the referring physician. This is a situation which the psychoanalyst deplores, but cannot change. There are many occasions when he would feel happier if he had the right to share his knowledge with others.

A few actual experiences, which are in no way exceptional, can best illustrate these difficulties. Neurotic problems are often dissimulated. More frequently than is realized, patients succeed for years in fooling their friends and families into thinking of them as people of more than ordinary stability and poise. They may carry responsibilities well. To the rest of the world, they may appear happy and successful. Yet all the while, and notwithstanding this courageous simulation of health, they may suffer almost continuously from neurotic symptoms which they never acknowledge. When such persons finally come to psychoanalysis these hidden symptoms may soon be aggravated, so that the patient looks and feels worse than before he began treatment. At this the patient usually will take his family and his physician into his confidence; which naturally gives rise to the impression that the analysis is making the patient worse. Actually this uncovering of hidden neurotic symptoms is an essential forward step, without which no healing can occur. This is one of the many situations in which it is wise whenever possible to give psychoanalytic patients a large measure of privacy from their customary contacts, and in which the well-meant solicitude of loyal friends may add a considerable burden of unnecessary strain.

A young business man is an example of just such a situation. He was a man of exceptional ability, who early in life had achieved unusual success. In addition he had carried the responsibilities of two households and managed the affairs of a large family, which looked up to him as to a figure of unshakable strength. No one but his wife had any suspicion that he was troubled by an array of phobias and by a severe psychosexual problem. For. the sake of the many people who were dependent on him, this patient had kept his symptoms secret, as well as the fact that he was being psychoanalyzed. Had anyone known of this, however, within a few weeks the cry would have been raised that under the influence of the analysis the patient was getting worse; because by that time his old symptoms were intensified, and in addition many new ones had come to light. Fortunately in this case there was nobody who could interfere; and the patient had an opportunity to work through this symptomatic flurry to reach lasting health.

Equally difficult for the outsider to judge fairly is the case of the patient who comes to analysis and attends each session faithfully, but never does a stroke of analytic work. Sometimes he comes and says only selected things, consistently refusing on the basis of one excuse or another to follow the rule of free association. In the end, after a period of conscientious effort, the psychoanalyst will discontinue such a

treatment. If the patient is seriously sick, however, the psychoanalyst may hang on doggedly, trying by every device at
his command to break through the patient's defenses and win
his confidence, because the analyst knows that, unless he succeeds, the patient will remain sick indefinitely. If he fails,
the outsider will think, "What a racket this is, all that time
and money for nothing"; and the defeated psychoanalyst is
not free to explain that although the patient came for many
months he may have done only a few days of honest analytical work in that entire period.

In another type of case the treatment is a race against time,
that is, a race against the downhill course of an illness which
has already acquired great momentum. For instance, certain
sudden disorders which if untreated will regularly lead to
serious mental illness, can sometimes be arrested by immediate psychoanalytic therapy. At some point, but rarely early
enough, the patient is brought to the psychoanalyst. If the
analyst has the courage to undertake the treatment of such
a patient, he knows that he is entering a race which is difficult
to win. Occasionally he will succeed in cutting short the
attack and in returning the patient to health before he has to
go through the entire cycle of illness. More frequently, however, before the analysis is even fairly launched, the patient
may become so disturbed as to require hospitalization, either
temporary or permanent.

An example of this type of experience is the case of a man
in his middle forties, who had been subject to recurrent
periods of severe emotional illness for nearly twenty-five
years. In the incipient stages of a fresh attack, this patient
was placed under treatment in the hands of an able colleague.
In a short time, however, despite this analytic interference,
the patient had to be hospitalized for a few weeks. When
this happened some of his closest friends and relatives
became alarmed, and claimed that the psychoanalyst had
caused the illness. Completely overlooking the fact that identical episodes of illness had occurred many times before psy-

choanalysis had ever been contemplated, they tried unsuccess-
fully to influence the patient's wife to interrupt the treatment.
After a few weeks of hospitalization, however, the patient
improved sufficiently to enable him to return to his analysis,
at first continuing to live in the hospital, and later in his own
home. It was soon found that the analytical work that had
been done before the severe upset related itself immediately
to that which was done during the convalescence. The final
outcome of the two together was a return to uninterrupted
health. In this case it was only the wife's firm confidence
in the psychoanalyst that prevented a premature interruption
of the treatment.

Perhaps more difficult to evaluate than any of the foregoing, however, is the problem of the forlorn hope. There
are desperate illnesses in the field of psychiatry, just as there
are in other medical fields. That is to say, there are illnesses
which are so severe that the patient almost never makes a
complete recovery, or at best, remains a crippled personality
for the rest of his days. Sometimes such conditions develop
out of seemingly innocent and insignificant neurotic disturbances. A patient may be brought to psychoanalysis for
troubles which the family and the family physician look upon
as trivial, when the patient may actually be on the brink of an
incurable mental illness. Here the diagnostic keenness of the
psychoanalyst is of vital importance; and it is here that the
adequacy of his fundamental psychiatric training is put to the
test. If the pathological process has not gained too much
headway, after frank discussion of the dangers with the
referring physician and some responsible representative of the
family, the psychoanalyst may attempt to check the progress
of the disease. Under such circumstances it is rare that anyone but the official representative of the family realizes
that the psychoanalyst is knowingly undertaking a forlorn
hope and that his chances of success are slight. Yet if no
analyst is willing to take this risk, the patient may be deprived
of his only chance of escaping permanent sickness. In such

situations those who are on the inside tend to keep their knowledge to themselves; and in the event of failure, it therefore appears to the rest of the world as though a slightly nervous person has been driven into permanent illness by psychoanalytic intervention.

For instance, a severe case of paranoia was already well-developed before the patient was brought to a psychiatrist. Nevertheless, to the casual observer the patient still seemed merely "a little nervous". At the insistence of the family the patient was subjected to a cautious psychoanalytic investigation, which was abruptly interrupted by the family after only a few weeks. Two years later, when the patient required permanent hospitalization, this was blamed by many outsiders on the few weeks of tentative psychoanalytic probing. Psychoanalysis cannot claim to be that potent, whether for good or for evil.

A less subtle source of trouble for the psychoanalyst is the patient who comes with impossible hopes as to what analysis should do for him, cravings which he may not relinquish despite the fact that they are not attainable by anything short of magic. Unless the analysis succeeds in uncovering and resolving these fantasies, such a patient usually goes away disgruntled, even when he may have been relieved of serious symptoms. For instance, an artist in his middle thirties came to a psychoanalyst for the treatment of a neurosis which had had its symptomatic onset before he was fifteen years of age. He was a man of outstanding ability, who had on several occasions been offered important positions in the world of art. On each occasion, however, his acute anxiety states, his fantastic compulsions, his neurotic seclusiveness and hostility, and his disordered psychosexual life, prevented his realizing his ambitions. When he came to the psychoanalyst he had been unable to work for almost a year, because of a purely imaginary (i.e., "hysterical") paralysis of one of his arms. As a result he and his family were on the verge of starvation. For many months he was treated without charge, and during the course of that work was able to resume his craft. He secured a good position in commercial art, so that he could support himself and his children. The larger part of his neurotic symptoms were reduced to negligible severity, although they were not completely removed. In fact, at the end the patient acknowledged that he clung almost deliberately to the remaining symptom, chiefly as an excuse for not pursuing his earlier ambitions. Nevertheless, and in spite of his obvious improvement, after an unavoidable interruption of his analysis this patient became hostile. Because the psychoanalyst had not set the hands of the clock back twenty years, so as to make him again the prodigy which he once had been, he inveighed against psychoanalysis and the psychoanalyst. In these attacks he stressed only the large amount of time which he had contributed to his treatment. Furthermore, as evidence of his unimproved condition he pointed to the fact that he was still unable to realize his earlier ambitions. He would not mention the severe and crippling symptoms which had disturbed his entire life, throwing him out of work and rendering him helpless and penniless, and of which to all intents and purposes he had been relieved. His hearers heard only what he chose to tell them, and misjudged the value of his analytic experience accordingly.

With the patient and his family hedging his illness around with secrecy and sometimes even with deception, it is small wonder that the outside world watches the progress of an analysis and its outcome with skepticism and misgivings. One can meet this only by urging the onlookers to bear in mind that it is impossible to judge the outcome except in the light of full information, and that they can only rarely be in possession of this information.

It has already been seen that the family physician can be taken into the analyst's confidence only with care and reservation (Chapter XIII). This is even more necessary in dealing with family and friends. Often enough friends and relatives may be a focal point in the patient's neurosis, and contact with them may stir up symptomatic activity long after this has disappeared in all other situations. That is one reason why so many patients can maintain a pretense of health in the presence of the outside world long after their families are well aware of their illnesses; and it is also why patients who may show marked improvement on the outside, continue to exhibit their old difficulties at home. Neuroses arise in the bosom of the family, and persist there with greatest tenacity. This is not calculated to arouse in the families of patients much confidence in the therapeutic value of the analysis. It is likely rather to give them a one-sided and pessimistic picture of the patient's progress. Furthermore, despite adequate warnings, it is hard for the family and friends to believe that in the treatment of a neurosis, by whatever method, a patient must get worse before he gets better. Yet this occurs inevitably, because every human being shields himself as well as he can from that which is neurotic in his nature; so that every patient must first go through the painful and distressing experience of facing unsuspected depths of illness before he begins to turn towards health. This initial and sometimes recurring intensification of symptoms may be serious enough to cause grave concern to family and friends and medical advisers; yet it is something for which everyone who faces an analysis must be prepared.

At times patients who have had full-blown psychotic episodes should be treated psychoanalytically during their intervals of health, in an effort to avoid further recurrences. In such situations the referring physician and responsible representatives of the family should be warned that psychotic episodes may occur at almost any time during the course of the analysis and sometimes with little warning, and that it may be only after several such episodes have been analyzed that the patient's health will become in any degree secure. Without such warnings, misunderstandings are almost certain to arise which can lead to premature interruption of the work.

The Right of Consultation

This is not an argument that, merely because the facts are so rarely accessible to the critic, one should never criticize or question or doubt an analyst. Analysts are far from infallible, and mistakes occur in analyses as they do in any other form of medical therapy. Fortunately there is a constructive way of intervening. Granting that before undertaking the analysis it is essential to have every possible assurance as to the integrity and ability of the psychoanalyst who is chosen, and granting also that it is wise thereafter to leave things in his hands, nevertheless situations arise in which the inalienable right of any patient and family to a consultation should be exercised. The only question is how to do this in such a way that the further therapeutic usefulness of the psychoanalyst will not be impaired. A simple course can be recommended:

(a) If this was not done at the beginning, it is essential to ascertain from a psychoanalytic society whether the particular physician is an adequately trained psychoanalyst.

(b) The next step would be to go directly to the psychoanalyst himself with all of one's doubts and questions.

(c) If this does not allay the anxiety that has arisen, one may then ask for a consultation with another psychoanalyst and the family physician. In arranging such a consultation it is best to work out with the original psychoanalyst and the consultants how and when and whether the patient himself should be examined. In fact, unless there is reasonable doubt as to the integrity and competence of the psychoanalyst in question, it is often well to defer any direct examination of the patient until after a preliminary conference between the psychoanalyst, the consultants, and the representatives of the patient. Sometimes the detailed discussion of the story of the illness and of the course of the treatment may make unnecessary any examination of the patient himself. This at times has great advantages.

One cannot be sure that these steps will always settle the disquieting issues; but it is as fair and safe a procedure as can be followed.   Fortunately such steps are necessary only rarely, and in exceptional cases.

Some Reasons for Failure

For his own guidance the psychoanalyst could summarize as follows some typical causes of analytic defeats:

(1) Those which are due to faulty technique, and faulty diagnosis, etc.   They can be reduced to a minimum by turning only to properly trained men.

(2) Analyses which fail for external reasons, in spite of the fact that they have been soundly conducted:

(a) Because they have been prematurely interrupted by unavoidable external circumstances;

(b) Because they have been prematurely interrupted as a result of the impatient interference of those who influence the patient.   This can sometimes be avoided when it is possible to give accurate warnings to the referring physician and to the responsible members of the family as to what to expect; and where the family is sufficiently stable to hold to a course once it is agreed upon.

(3) Soundly conducted analyses which fail because of forces inherent in the illness which is being treated:

(a) Where the psychoanalyst has made a legitimate but unsuccessful effort to save a patient who was already desperately ill, i.e., the "forlorn hope";

(b) Those which fail, but only temporarily, because in a race to stave off a process which has already gained too much momentum the analysis loses.   Such temporary failures may in the end turn out to be sound successes, if in a later and less stormy phase of the illness the analysis can be resumed and carried through to completion.

(4) Analyses which fail because of forces peculiar to particular cases:

(a) Where a patient who suffers from an otherwise curable neurosis cannot be induced by the psychoanalyst to undergo those essential emotional deprivations without which no real analysis is possible;

(b) Where the life situation of a patient is so unalterably unfortunate that life itself can offer nothing better to the patient than the retreat afforded by the neurosis;

(The first group is sometimes represented by patients who have been spoiled by great wealth; and the second group by certain sufferers from great poverty. Subtler factors than these, however, may also play a determining role.)

(c) Where a patient has so many positive assets, that with every minor advance he feels convinced that he is well. There may be a complete if temporary disappearance of all symptoms, and the patient reaches a plateau of apparent health while the analysis stalls.

(5) Analyses which fail because the patient cannot be induced to abandon deliberate plans to block the treatment:

(a) Where the patient comes to the analysis for months but can never be launched in the free production of his material;

(b) Where patients enter analysis reluctantly, under pressure from some external compulsion rather than because of an acknowledged internal need. Such patients often are firmly and unalterably resolved to withhold essential data, either in a deliberate effort to thwart the psychoanalyst and thus to take revenge on those who forced the analysis on them, or else to protect someone else;

(c) Where the patient has a secret but conscious determination not to get well, e.g., because he feels that recovery would be a tacit admission that the whole illness was psychological and therefore "his own fault", instead of being physical or due to external forces. To blame the body or the outside world is always a temptation to the patient who looks upon his neurosis as a sign of shameful weakness.

The list could be extended greatly to include many technical factors, until the reader, in confusion, would begin to wonder how it happens that psychoanalysis ever succeeds. One may offer assurances on this score, however, and couple them with the comment that one hears much less about psychoanalytic successes than about failures. Partly this is because the healed patient goes his way gratefully but quietly, so that few people may know the nature or extent of his previous difficulties, and even fewer may know that he had ever been under psychoanalytic treatment.

The Final Test of Health

After an analysis is over, however, it is fair to appeal to a wider court in evaluating its effects. Provided that the judges have any knowledge of why the patient sought analysis in the first place, it is fair to measure its results in terms of the patient's apparent happiness and peace, his satisfaction in his activities, his freedom from disturbing states of depression, anxiety, guilt, anger, fear, or jealousy, and finally and specifically his freedom from those neurotic symptoms which brought him to analysis in the first place.

Certainly it is not an analytic goal to alter fundamentally the life situation of every patient. The psychoanalyst hopes rather to make it possible for the patient to find health within the framework of the life which he is already living. This means that by and large the psychoanalyst prefers to leave marriages, occupations and friendships unaltered. On the other hand, as is explained in Chapters XI and XIX, this aim must always be secondary to the patient's health. Where a life has been built under the influence of neurotic mechanisms, nothing short of radical alterations may suffice to make health possible. In such situations the analysis becomes a surgical instrument, the psychoanalyst needs a surgeon's courage, and the patient the ability to endure pain. It takes a good surgeon to know when not to operate, and a good psychoanalyst to know when to leave things alone. But the final criterion of success is the health of the patient and not what has to be altered in the patient's life situation.

Such health, as we have already tried to indicate in Chapters II and III, expresses itself subtly in every aspect of life. The patient will have gained an enlarged understanding of himself and of all of those with whom his life comes into contact, a deeper understanding of his own children and of their needs, freedom to give of his time, energy and interest to the world at large, to his own business of living, and to his human relationships. He will have learned certain things about himself which many of his close friends could have told him, but which before his analysis he could not have understood. He might have recognized the words, but never the tune; and he would have been unable to use this knowledge, because he would still have been under the tyrannical domination of his own unconscious mechanisms. This indeed is the greatest of his analytic gains—a true inner freedom, a broadening of the areas of life in which psychological forces of whose nature he is now fully aware would dominate his thoughts and feelings and purposes and behavior. To the extent to which his analysis had succeeded, therefore, he would have become flexible, adaptable, and dynamically mature and free.

Chapter XVI

THE FINANCIAL ARRANGEMENTS FOR AN ANALYSIS

It is customary to pass lightly over the financial arrangements between a professional man and his client or patient, both behaving as though money did not exist, and as though it were below the dignity of either to discuss their financial arrangements frankly. This polite pretense is especially prevalent in the dealings between a physician and his patients. Even if he wanted to, however, the psychoanalyst could not follow such a course without jeopardizing the analysis.

It is the psychoanalyst's task to clarify to his patient the ways in which unconscious attitudes can disturb any aspect of his life. Therefore, the analyst can hardly permit his patient to evade the conscious and unconscious emotional significance of money. Nor could the analyst bring these unconscious attitudes into the open, if he and the patient danced a polite but evasive minuet about their financial arrangements. Indeed not infrequently it is in the way in which the patient plans to finance his analysis and the way in which he pays his monthly analytic bills, that the full complexity of his unconscious attitudes to money first becomes clear. Moreover, how this problem is handled may prove to be an important indicator of the nature of the patient's purposes in seeking treatment. Consequently, for psychological as well as practical reasons a full and frank discussion of finances is necessary when planning for an analysis.

The relationship of the psychoanalyst and his patient is in essence an unwritten mutual contract in which, as with any physician, the patient remains free to terminate his treatment at any time. It is the analyst's hope, however, that the patient will not do this impulsively, or without careful, joint deliberation. For as long as the patient chooses to remain in his care, the psychoanalyst, on his part, obligates himself to treat the patient in return for a certain agreed fee per session, and to remain responsible for that treatment until he feels that he has done everything in his power to help the patient towards health. The patient agrees to be financially responsible for the time assigned to him, whether he keeps his appointments or not, from the moment when he begins his analysis until it is either terminated or discontinued. At the end of each month the analyst presents a bill, usually directly to the patient, based on the number of sessions scheduled for that month. Nor, if he is wise, will he allow the patient politely to evade repeated discussions of these monthly accounts.

The Missed Session

Even where the patient announces in advance his intention to miss a session, he may still be held responsible for it. Otherwise the patient would be given a double incentive to miss appointments and to become irregular in attendance. Every patient has a natural temptation to avoid analytic sessions whenever things become difficult. Consequently, unless there is some strong deterrent, minor business or social demands may be allowed to interrupt the continuity of the analytical work, precisely when such interruptions will be most deleterious in their effects on the analysis. If the patient were not charged for appointments which he missed for inconsequential reasons, the analyst would, in effect, be offering him a financial inducement to escape painful sessions, since he could go off and enjoy himself, and save money as well. The steady, day-by-day continuity of analytical work is of such importance that every inducement must be brought to bear on a patient to hold him to his schedule, in spite of his natural impulse to break the work into discontinuous fragments. On the other hand, when a patient is well launched in treatment and works consistently and faithfully, the analyst need not adhere rigidly to the practice of charging for missed hours. In this matter, therefore, he is free to vary his practice, both from case to case and at different stages in the analysis of any patient.

Setting the Fee

It is never justifiable for a psychoanalyst to fix his charges at such a rate that all of the funds available for a patient's analysis will be used up within a few months, when a lower fee would carry the patient through a longer period of treatment to its successful termination. Therefore it is imperative to budget carefully for an adequate length of time. Although it is impossible ever to predict how long an analysis will take, it is a wise procedure to plan for at least two years of work, pointing out that it may take less than that, but stressing equally the possibility that it may take longer. To aid the psychoanalyst in fixing a fair fee, the patient will describe to him the facts concerning (1) his financial status, (2) his income, (3) his capital, (4) his prospects, (5) his responsibilities, and if necessary (6) any accessory sources of funds which might be made available to help him finance his treatment. These six items have to be taken into account in planning the financing of any analysis. The patient who will not trust his analyst with these financial facts might just as well not attempt to be analyzed, because he will surely not trust his analyst with more intimate data. The analyst on his part must insist on this information so that he can be fair to the patient as well as to his own needs, and also to put to an immediate test the willingness of the patient to trust him fully. Together then, with this information, they will decide what the fee should be, and whether it should be paid entirely by the patient himself, and entirely out of income.

Sometimes it is wise to look upon health as a form of capital, thus justifying the use of a certain amount of financial capital in paying for the treatment, so as to lessen the immediate sacrifices which paying for the analysis out of income alone would entail. Thus, a thousand dollars out of income in one year might cripple a family's budget; whereas if taken out of capital it would reduce the family income by only a few dollars a year. This spreads the cost of the analysis over the many years during which the patient and his family can expect to enjoy the benefits of it. Perhaps it is relevant to add that the psychoanalyst contributes working capital to every treatment, in that he gives his patients his only irreplaceable capital goods, *Time.* The hours which he devotes to his patients are his only working capital; and what he expends on one patient cannot be used for another. Therefore, when necessary, a similar contribution from the patient is not unreasonable, provided that such a capital outlay would not jeopardize the fundamental economic security of the patient and his family.

Sometimes it is difficult to decide who should pay for an analysis, or how the cost should be divided. In general it is best for a patient to pay for his own treatment. Frequently, however, wives or minors may have no money at all, or very little, whereas the husband, parent or guardian may have ample resources. In such cases the psychoanalyst and the prospective patient together consider whether any of these accessory sources may fairly be called upon to support the patient's treatment, or whether the use of any outside source will obstruct the progress of the analysis. This issue is decided individually in each case. For instance, one patient who was heir to a large fortune was treated for many months for a token fee. He could have gone freely to his father for money; but for this patient it happened to be essential that he should undertake his treatment on an independent and self-supporting basis, and that it should be his personal sacrifice alone which made the analysis possible. Consequently he was charged only what he himself could afford, an amount which would ordinarily be charged to a person of limited means. Analysts cannot always do this, however; because, when an analyst makes a reduction in his charges for the benefit of some patient who could turn to others for financial help, that analyst thereby limits his ability to make concessions to other impecunious patients whose friends and relatives have no funds with which to supplement the limited means of the patients. Therefore, although in the example cited this concession made a major contribution to the success of the treatment, it also limited the contribution which the analyst could make to others. Certainly mere embarrassment at the idea of asking someone for financial help is never an adequate reason for allowing a patient to pay less than the financial status of his family as a whole would justify.

Consequently from the social point of view a patient should be ready to borrow in order to pay for his analysis, if his own funds are not sufficient and if others to whom he is close have ample funds, whenever this will not hinder the analysis. If a patient who could borrow fails to do so, and the analyst therefore treats him for little or nothing, in effect the patient is being treated at the expense of other poorer patients for whom no accessory funds are available. There are few psychoanalysts who can themselves afford to play the role of banker; but even if they could, such a relationship would seriously hamper the analysis.

Psychoanalytic fees vary widely. The same psychoanalyst will have at one time one patient who is paying him nothing, another who pays five cents an hour, and a third who pays twenty-five or thirty dollars an hour. There is no one "fair" charge. A surgeon may be entitled to charge many hundreds of dollars for one hour of his operative skill; the psychoanalyst's apprenticeship takes even longer than that of the skilled surgeon. The surgeon, however, makes his charge only once; whereas the psychoanalyst's fee goes on for many months or even years. Therefore, as we have said, the analyst charges only what a patient can afford to pay for as long as the analysis is likely to last, and whatever arrangement the analyst makes should enable the patient to finance the analysis to its termination. He must take into consideration the source of the money with which he is being paid, so that this, in turn, will not in any way hamper the progress of the work; and he must provide the patient with an opportunity to make some personal sacrifice for the analysis. To this end, when a patient does not pay the entire fee himself, he can be charged with the responsibility for some part of it at least.

Like anyone else, the psychoanalyst must earn a reasonable, steady income from his day's work. It is rarely possible for anyone to analyze more than eight to ten patients at a time and do them full justice. From the varying fees which these patients are charged, the analyst must realize a certain average return. Therefore he must balance each patient who is unable to pay him more than a fraction of this average with one who can pay him above the average. When, on the other hand, his list includes several patients who pay average or higher than average fees, it becomes possible for him to work with other patients for little or nothing. Almost every psychoanalyst carries a few patients in this latter category, except for those who make their contribution to society by giving time to hospitals and to teaching, without compensation. It is the rule of some psychoanalytic societies to exact a pledge from every member to accept at least one free patient who is referred from the Psychoanalytic Institute. Where no such pledge is exacted, much the same contribution is made through the personal recommendation of poor patients from one psychoanalyst to another on a voluntary basis. That is, a psychoanalyst whose schedule is full, or who cannot afford at a particular time to take on another free patient, guides such a patient to another psychoanalyst whose schedule makes it possible to accept him.

It has long been argued by some analysts that for a variety of reasons an analysis for which a patient makes no personal financial sacrifice is foredoomed to failure. This has not been the experience of the author. It is true, of course, that a patient may exploit an analyst's generosity for neurotic reasons. This neurotic drive may defy analysis for many months, because of the gratification which the patient derives from this behavior. Usually, however, such analytic generosity bears fruit in the end, as the patient begins to face his guilt, and the reasons for it. However, this entire issue of the therapeutic leverage of the free analysis requires critical re-investigation.

Average Fees and Average Costs

We have said that the psychoanalysts' fee may range from zero to twenty-five or thirty dollars per session or, in exceptional circumstances, even higher. In 1936 the average fee for all psychoanalytical work done in New York City was under ten dollars an hour. Today the average fees are somewhat higher. In the winter of 1948–49 a questionnaire was sent to every member of the American Psychoanalytic Association. Usable answers were received from about 42 per cent of the membership. They revealed a number of interesting facts: e.g. for the United States as a whole the average fee per session was $14.50. The range, from 0 to $50.00, was distributed as follows: *

Percentage of all patients under analysis		Fees paid by patients under analysis	
2.5%	paid	less than	$ 5.00 per session
7.4%	"	$ 5.00 through $ 9.00 " "
31.5%	"	$10.00 " $14.00 " "
35.6%	"	$15.00 " "
12.1%	"	$20.00 " "
8.1%	"	$25.00 " "
2.3%	"	$30.00 through $39.00 " "
0.5%	"	$40.00 " $50.00 " "

Among the various psychoanalytic centers there was less variation in the averages than had been anticipated. The range was from $11.30 in one city, to just about $18.00 in another, with the other large centers all averaging between $12.00 and $17.00.

Since only 42 per cent of the membership furnished usable information, it is not possible to claim absolute accuracy for

* Reported in detail in *Psychiatry*, Vol. XIII, No. 2, 1950, pp. 227–445.

these statistics. We have no way of knowing whether those who answered represent a random sample of the whole group, or whether the "high-chargers" or "the low-chargers" held back disproportionately. Since the replies were all anonymous, however, it is probable, that these figures are reasonably accurate. If statistics were available on the cost of analyses conducted under supervision by advanced students (cf. Chapter XXII), the percentage of analyses at less than $10.00 per session would be enormously increased for every training center.

If these charges are compared with the consultation fees charged by most medical specialists, they are modest enough; and compared with a surgeon's charges, they are minute. But when one takes into consideration the fact that the patient must pay this fee for not merely once, but every day for many weeks and months or even years, it is clear that the ultimate cost is high. The exact amount will vary, of course, both with the fee per session and with the duration of the analysis. If one year is taken as a basis of computation, eliminating Sundays, most Saturdays, and at least one month's holiday in the summer and a few shorter interruptions, there will be about 200 to 225 analytic sessions in the analytic year. At ten dollars per session this will cost $2,000 to $2,250 for a year's analytical work. At higher or lower rates the total expense will vary proportionately.

Peculiarities of the Psychoanalyst's Economic Position

In spite of the fact that even at low rates the total expense for the patient is heavy, the analyst does not earn a large income. The psychoanalyst who sticks to his job, who does not accept too many consultations (since these break into the continuity of his therapeutic schedule), who works consistently with the same patients, who does not give his patients fewer sessions per week merely to make it possible to charge higher fees per session, and who does not crowd his days with too many patients—such an analyst cannot earn an income comparable to that of the successful consultant in internal medicine, the surgeon, or almost any other specialist. Indeed, the psychoanalyst's economic position tends to be somewhat precarious. Because his income is derived from work with a few patients at a time, it is relatively easy for him to become established on a modest basis. On the other hand, this income will fluctuate sharply as patients start or stop. In times of economic unrest it is not a rare experience for patients who have been economically secure to be deprived of important sources of income suddenly in the midst of treatment, or to have to undertake unexpected financial responsibilites for other members of their families. It is then a matter of conscience for the psychoanalyst to carry that patient at a reduced fee for as long as possible, and not to drop him at a critical point in his analysis simply because of his lack of funds. The psychoanalyst is willing to do this for a few patients; but if he attempts to help many patients in this way, he may find that several hours of every day are devoted to uncompensated work. The psychoanalyst's own economic security will then be undermined, and he can make himself secure only by taking on more patients than he can treat with maximal efficiency, or by interrupting the analyses of some of his poorer patients in order to replace them with others who are more fortunately placed. No conscientious analyst does this unless he is forced to; but there is a limit beyond which he cannot go without impairing his own security, his peace of mind, and the quality of his work. This dilemma is always painful, but until there are endowment funds for the support of analyses of indigent patients, psychoanalysts will have to compromise as best they can between their own needs and their responsibility to their analysands.

The economic position of the analyst is unusual in one other respect. His years of training last until he is between thirty-five and forty. Another few years are required before he gains full clinical maturity. Therefore a life-expectancy which, after the age of fifty-five, drops below that of most other professional groups does not give him many years in which to serve the community, or in which to earn an education for his children or a modest independent security for his own old age. This has an effect on what he must try to accumulate during his relatively few earning years, and therefore on what he must charge for his services, and on how much free work he can do. These facts create a serious problem in medical economics which cannot be solved by analysts alone, but only by the coordinated efforts of the whole community.

Some Additional Comments

The survey cited in the preceding pages seems to contain the most recent conclusive data available regarding the cost of analytic therapy. However, indirect data derived from probability deductions from the costs of training analyses are found in a survey made by Doctors Bertram D. Lewin and Helen Ross recently.* These suggest that the current average cost of analysis in the United States is probably a little more than $20 per hour.

* A Survey of Psychoanalytic Education in the United States (W. W. Norton & Company, New York, 1960, pp. 105–107).

III. *Some General Considerations*

Chapter XVII

THE CONTRAST BETWEEN PSYCHOANALYSIS AND HEALING BY FAITH OR BY SUGGESTION

Psychoanalysis Not a Cure by Suggestion, Faith, or Confession

Many years ago Claude Bernard, the great French physiologist, pointed out that philosophers, theologians, and scientists are all alike as human beings; and that since they are human their minds obey the same basic laws. Thus, all of us operate under the influence of biases, prejudices and preconceptions, and in our work we make use of variable mixtures of logic, guesswork, and intuition. Out of this our theories arise, whether these are scientific, philosophical or theological. What then distinguishes the followers of these disciplines from one another? Claude Bernard pointed out that the scientist stands apart from the rest in only one important respect. If he is a true scientist, then the mere fact that any theory is his own, or that it seems or "feels" true and convincing, has no value for him as evidence. For the scientist no theory, however logical, can ever be more than the starting point for an investigation. As this great physiologist put it, the scientist sheds his theories with his coat as he enters his laboratory; and not even logic is a substitute for evidence.

The psychoanalyst maintains the same scientific attitude. When he interprets to a patient some bit of behavior, or a fragment of his life-story, or a dream, that interpretation is put forward not as an article of faith but as a working hypothesis, a theory which might conceivably explain the psychological experience. It is something to be tested against the patient's further material. What the patient produces at the time of the interpretation or in the subsequent course of the analysis will either confirm the hypothesis, or correct it, or throw it into the discard.

Therefore the psychoanalyst expects and invites from his patients a frank and open skepticism. Nothing excites graver misgivings in him than the blind credulity and pious faith which some earnest patients struggle to maintain. Experience has taught the analyst that unless he can break down such attitudes they will make lasting therapeutic results impossible. He knows that the patient's effort to look upon him as omniscient and omnipotent is a symptom of the patient's neurosis, a direct carry-over from infancy; and he sets out not to exploit this uncritical worship but to analyze it away. All of this is quite different from the attitude and practice of the faith-healer.

All methods of healing by faith have in common certain fundamental assumptions and processes. First there is a basic premise that recovery depends upon supernatural forces which affect all illnesses equally. As a consequence of this, it is superfluous to make a differential diagnosis, and no detailed investigation of the natural phenomena of disease is necessary. Indeed, since all that is needed is faith in the supernatural force in order to call it into action on the side of a mystical healing process, one need not bother even to take a careful history, or to make a careful physical, psychological or laboratory study. Therefore the faith-healer never knows what, if anything, he is "healing." In contrast to this, the psychoanalyst bases his therapy upon the detailed investigation and evaluation of each case as an individual problem. Indeed, even during the course of the analysis there may be long months of study before definitive therapy gets under way.

Secondly, all methods of healing by faith or magic depend upon some form of exhortation, a mobilizing of religious and personal emotional enthusiasms. This is not the technical meaning of "suggestion," but this is what the word connotes to most laymen: i.e., an emotional ecstasy which carries the patient out of one mood and into another, and in so doing obscures or gets rid of his symptoms, at least for the time being. To the layman, suggestion also connotes the influence of ideas to which the patient has been introduced by the "healer." Such ideas may influence the patient by challenging the logic of his own thinking; or they may exercise their influence largely through the emotional hold of the person who has presented them, and irrespective of their objective validity. This emotional influence may in turn be conscious or unconscious, deliberate or inadvertent; and it may lead the patient to accept ideas without any effort at personal critical evaluation. Thus the operation of suggestion in this sense is always dependent on the human relationship behind the ideas, a relationship which induces the patient to abrogate his right to individual judgment. Consequently, once the relationship is broken the patient will sooner or later regurgitate the imposed ideas. This is one reason why hypnotism, in its original form of direct suggestion, failed to produce lasting therapeutic results. The psychoanalyst, instead of making use of suggestion in this fashion, is constantly on the lookout to combat any manifestation of a tendency to submissive suggestibility on the part of the patient. Much incompetent and some skillful palliative psychotherapy depends largely upon suggestive procedures. Nothing however could be further from the theory and practice of competent Freudian psychoanalysis.

It may be argued, on the other hand, that psychoanalysis also works through a human relationship. This is true; but the bond is utilized differently. In analysis the relationship between the patient and the physician is not used to influence the patient directly, but rather to facilitate the production of buried material which would otherwise remain inaccessible. As is explained in the discussion of the analysis of the transference, every effort is made in analytic therapy not to bind the patient to the analyst or to his fantasies about the analyst, but rather to clarify these fantasies so as to enable the patient to progress steadily towards greater freedom.

Let me repeat that what psychoanalysis demands of the patient is diametrically opposite to that which faith-healing demands. Psychoanalysis demands confidence in the integrity and intelligence of the analyst, an intellectual willingness to cooperate, and a wholehearted purpose to abide by the rule of the analysis that the patient produce material freely and honestly. This in turn requires a courageous willingness to accept pain, anxiety, and deprivation, and to face unpleasant facts. Psychoanalysis, however, not only does not demand blind faith, it attempts constantly to analyze it away, even when this is faith in the analysis itself. Credulity impedes the progress of analytic therapy and insight, by hiding secret disagreements under a mask of sham compliance.

Psychoanalysis also demands willingness to accept in every detail the reality of the body, in a fashion which contrasts sharply with the faith-healer's effort to deny the reality of organic disease. Therefore, even where the faith-healer succeeds temporarily in suppressing pain, the analyst views this not as a therapeutic achievement but as the reinforcement of a process of illness; since suppressed pain is not eliminated from psychic life but is certain to reappear in other forms and at other times with increased intensity.

In all of these fundamental respects, therefore, psychoanalysis and healing by faith or by suggestion are at opposite poles.

Illusory Faith Cures

This is not the place to discuss the many claims which have been made for the power of healing by faith. It is well to remind ourselves, however, that in evaluating such stories it is at least as difficult as in psychoanalysis for the outsider to know what condition was treated, what changes may occur spontaneously in such conditions, and what was the real relationship of the treatment to the course of the illness. Every psychiatrist has had the experience of treating a patient who was convalescing slowly. Sometimes in such cases some well-meaning friend or relative will make the suggestion that the patient should turn to some form of faith-cure. If the patient had attempted this during the deeper stages of his illness, it would have brought him no relief. As his convalescence progresses, however, the patient's growing optimism makes it possible for him to respond to any hopeful philosophy; and as this happens he may find himself seizing hold of Christian Science or some other faith-healing cult. This gives him a further boost, and when recovery supervenes the patient may feel convinced that he was cured by faith; whereas, in reality, his ability to embrace the optimistic faith was the clear indication that his convalescence was well under way.

In general, one finds that so-called "cures" by faith-healing or by suggestion usually consist of a temporary alleviation of symptoms; and as we have said elsewhere, the curing of a symptom may mean the obscuring of an illness. In the long run, this may do serious harm to a patient who would otherwise have had a chance to rid himself of the underlying neurotic process. Occasionally, however, affiliation with a religious sect may be part of a more fundamental alteration in a distorted personality, a change sufficiently profound to place it on a sound basis as long as the faith persists. Such experiences carry an important lesson for the student of the psychotherapeutic process.

Psychotherapy and the Process of Conversion

One of the greatest obstacles to psychoanalytic therapy is the fact that we are a stiff-necked people. Every human being wants to be rid of pain; but at the bottom of his heart no human being really wants to change. It is the everyday experience of analysts to be consulted by patients who are in a state of severe mental suffering, but who nonetheless say to the analyst, "I would not mind being analyzed in order to

get rid of this suffering, but I do not want to be different."
Sometimes this desire not to change is conscious; sometimes
it is deeply buried; but it is always there. It constitutes one
of the most tenacious obstacles to therapy, for the simple
reason that neurotic symptoms are always the sparks from the
wheel of a neurotic personality. It is impossible to get rid
of a patient's symptoms if he cannot be led to accept humbly
and willingly the fact that he must struggle to become a different kind of person.

This humility, this willingness to change and to become
different, is something which sometimes is seen most clearly
in the process of religious conversion. Indeed, as psychoanalysts we must say with all humility that a true religious
leader can sometimes create in the hearts of his followers
a humble need for a different way of life which is often difficult for the analyst to achieve in his patient. It sometimes
happens, therefore, that a religious leader will succeed in
awakening a need to be different, without having the technical
equipment which will enable him to show his "patient"
specifically what needs to be changed and in what direction he
must change. The psychoanalyst on the other hand has these
techniques at his command, but may find it more difficult
to evoke in his patient the humble willingness to change
which is such an important part of the therapeutic process.
It would seem that each could learn something from the other,
and thus fuse into one healing process the essential elements
of the technique of conversion and the essential elements of
the technique of psychoanalytic therapy.

Psychoanalysis and Religious Faith

The relationship between science and religious faith has
troubled many minds for many years. This is not because
the problem itself is intricate, but rather because people often
dislike the conclusions to which their own logic brings them,
and therefore seek philosophic roads to conclusions which

they prefer. The issues themselves are reasonably simple and clear.

Science is an effort to find approximations of truth about ourselves and the world in which we live. Science depends upon methods of gathering empirical data, methods of testing the degree to which these data conform to external realities, thus establishing approximate "facts", methods of interpreting causal relationships between such approximate facts, and finally methods of testing the accuracy of these interpretations by efforts to predict future events. Science accepts nothing as valid until it is supported by evidence of this general nature. Thus the essential spirit of science is embodied in the basic principle that truth is always relative, always an approximation to reality, and that its acceptance always waits on evidence.

Religious faith, on the other hand, requires no evidence. For it, truth is established by the act of faith itself: and belief itself is the direct perception of a divinely revealed truth. Faith therefore is not a search but an acceptance for which no evidence is required. Indeed, dependence upon evidence should logically be regarded as faithless and irreligious. To demand proof of the existence of God would seem to deny Him by implying that He is just a theory like any other, to be tested by evidence. Consequently whether he realizes it or not, a scientist who has religious faith divides his universe into two kingdoms: the kingdom of science and the kingdom of faith. In the one he functions as a scientist, accepting nothing without scientific evidence. In the other he functions by faith alone.

Individual scientists vary in their willingness to divide the phenomenological world into these two kingdoms. There are some who hold that the scientific search for truth constitutes in their lives the equivalent of religion. If their philosophical self-scrutiny is mature, they will recognize that they base their life-work on certain tacit assumptions; but if they are consistent in their scientific spirit, they will use these assumptions only as working hypotheses to be tested and discarded whenever contrary evidence comes to light. As Claude Bernard said: to the scientist the fact that he believes or feels that something is true does not have the value of evidence; and he doffs his theories with his overcoat as he enters his laboratory. As a matter of fact, it is precisely this willingness to test and discard one's premises, which characterizes the scientific spirit as opposed to the spirit of religious faith. The two attitudes would seem to be mutually exclusive; yet there have always been some scientists who worship in a spirit of true faith. They are found among physicists, chemists, biologists, physicians, psychiatrists, and also among psychoanalysts.

Nevertheless, the relationship of psychoanalysis to faith differs in one respect from that of other sciences. Since psychoanalysis studies all psychological processes, it includes in the scope of its investigations the conscious and unconscious determinants both of faith and of skeptical doubt. For the analyst, faith and doubt like all other psychological processes are equally objects of scientific inquiry. They are studied in a broad context, however, of the dynamics of all forms of confidence and the lack of it, of trust and distrust, of credulity and suspiciousness.

In his study of the conscious and unconscious determinants of faith, the analyst traces its genesis and development in the life of the individual. Early in life the small child finds his main security against terror by trusting in parents, whose omnipotence and omniscience he quite unconsciously takes for granted. Subsequently, as this first childish "faith" wanes, he may never again trust anyone to the same degree, or he may for a time endow others with similar powers, temporarily placing his faith in teachers or in other older members of his family, or in mankind in general. At some point, however, he turns with his faith to some remote, unseen, supernatural, superhuman, yet more or less personalized power: witch, fairy, ogre, magician, devil, or God. His identification with his parents and their fears and faiths will play an important role in this. The analyst studies the extent to which this dependence upon external omnipotence is an expression of the child's neurotic anxiety or to what extent it may be the expression of other inner conflicts, such as the child's need for protection against his own destructive impulses. He investigates the form which the child's "faith" assumes, to see whether it is a learned pattern or is generated spontaneously. In other words, the analyst studies how each child creates his varying images of heaven and of hell, and his different concepts of supernatural powers who can reward and punish him in his struggle between fear and doubt and rage on the one hand, and faith and trust and love on the other.

The analyst recognizes furthermore that our social structure and in some measure our lives depend upon our ability to accept some things on trust. For instance, we go through each day with a tacit assumption that we will be here tomorrow. These are unnoticed acts of faith, which occur in every man's life, even in those who have no conscious faith in an omnipotent supernatural power, and they are closely related to his balance of unconscious fear and unconscious confidence. Some men trust everything and everyone; some men trust nothing and no one. Most men are mixed. There can be trust and distrust in the integrity and goodwill of other men, trust and distrust in the vulnerability of one's own body, trust and distrust in one's own integrity and goodwill. Consequently, viewed as a psychological process, faith in a supernatural omnipotent power and agnosticism are both special forms of the more general processes of faith or doubt. There are individuals who have quiet confidence in their fellowmen but none in any supernatural or omnipotent power; others who have religious faith in an omnipotent supernatural power, but none either in themselves or in human beings around them. Furthermore there are people who are consciously devout but unconscious skeptics, and conversely others who are consciously agnostic, yet unconsciously extremely devout. Thus doubters and trusters are to be found both among the devout and among the religiously agnostic.

Such clinical facts as these about the varieties of the religious experience challenge the analyst as something which he must study with an open mind if he is to understand the religious process in the human spirit. For most analysts this tends necessarily to bring faith under scientific scrutiny to a somewhat greater extent than is true for other scientists. There are a few analysts, however, who segregate religious faith in a separate phenomenological world of its own, placing it quite outside of the realm of scientific inquiry.

Chapter XVIII

PSYCHOANALYSIS AND MORAL RESPONSIBILITY

"You may not be responsible for getting into a mess, not the first
time at any rate; but who else is responsible for getting you out, and
what's more, for knocking enough sense into your head to keep you out!"

The charge is sometimes brought that in his consistent
efforts to explain immoral behavior the psychoanalyst aban-
dons the concept of human responsibility, destroys the distinction between good and evil, and merely gives his patient
"an easy out". Those who make these charges frequently
call analytic explanations of the mechanisms of anti-social
behavior "mere excuses". They point out that in his therapeutic work the psychoanalyst does not chide his patients for
misconduct nor exhort them to be better; and they cite this
as evidence of a supposedly immoral or amoral attitude on
the part of the analyst. The reasons why the analyst avoids
moralizing during treatment are outlined below. In the
meantime, however, we may point out that those critics overlook the fact that the analyst studies in his patients the genesis
of both their moral and their amoral behavior, hoping through
these studies to improve the techniques of ethical education.
This is an area in which improvements are sorely needed, if
we are to make moral education more effective than the
traditional methods of the past have proved.

However, psychoanalysis is changing our concepts of moral
responsibility in certain respects. For instance, it recognizes
that feelings of guilt or of virtue are by no means synony-
mous with actual guilt or actual goodness. Many people who
should feel guilt feel none and behave as though they were
the most moral folk in the world, or else they are indifferent
to or unaware of the destructive consequences of their behavior. The analyst tries to help such an individual to bring his
buried feelings of guilt out into the light, so as to modify the

disturbed behavior which they cause. Conversely, there are people who are haunted by feelings of guilt when they have no actual sins on their records. Every policeman is familiar with the man who gives himself up for a crime he did not commit. Every priest deals with penitents who come to confession weighed down with an inexplicable sense of sin. Here the function of the analyst is to help the patient to find the roots of his unreal and fantastic feelings of guilt. Thus, instead of providing an "easy out", the analyst attempts to bring the feelings of guilt and of moral responsibility into harmony with reality.

Furthermore psychoanalysis formulates the concept of moral responsibility in terms appropriate to each phase of human development, and in relation to two specific issues: (a) the degree of insight into unconscious psychological forces; and (b) the degree of freedom from compulsive mechanisms. Both of these elements in moral responsibility will be discussed in detail.

The Failure of Repression

One of the tragedies of our civilization arises from the fact that for so long the great religions of the world confused morality with ignorance of ourselves. The more "moral" and "civilized" man has become, the less has he known about himself, and the more urgently has he been taught to bury his primitive drives. That which he hides, however, always finds some way of expressing itself in indirect and symbolic patterns of thought, feeling, and behavior; and, as we have indicated in Chapter III, symbolic acts never satisfy, and consequently must be repeated compulsively.

Analysis has demonstrated that, whether we are dealing with fundamental instinctual needs or with the complex compulsive drives which are built on the fundamental instincts, it is costly and dangerous to attempt to manage such impulses by becoming unaware of their existence; because once they are driven underground, they lead to neurosis or delinquency. From this fact, however, the analyst does not draw the fallacious conclusion which is so often attributed to him, namely that all of our drives should be given free rein. Right here, let it be clearly understood that although analysis is against repression as a technique of self-mastery, it does not stand for self-indulgence or unlimited gratification.

On the contrary, psychoanalysts know perhaps better than anyone else that, just as the world could not achieve peace by appeasing Hitler, so too the human being cannot achieve peace by appeasing a neurosis through the unlimited indulgence of it. Freud pointed out repeatedly that the pleasure principle must be subordinated to the reality principle. But if this restraint is to lead to health and strength, it must be achieved through conscious mastery and not through repression into the unconscious. Furthermore, the analyst keeps in mind the fact that asceticism can serve purposes quite as neurotic as those of unlimited or compulsively driven license. Therefore he endorses neither extreme.

The relationship of insight to moral responsibility must also be considered in relation to age and maturity. It was St. Augustine who pointed out that the so-called innocence of the child is due more to the weakness of his limbs than to the purity of his heart. Thus, even before psychoanalysis existed, the Church had recognized that there are stormy elements in the infant which, unless they are adequately dealt with, can become a major source of distortions in our later ethical and emotional development. The psychoanalyst and the church both recognize that the child is engaged from his earliest years in a violent ethical struggle with the primitive amoral drives of infancy. Up to this point the Church doctrine and psychoanalytic observations coincide. The Church, however, looks upon this manifestation of infant psychology as an inherited sinfulness which merits punishment even before the age of reason, which is usually placed at about seven in church doctrines. The infant who dies unbaptized is consigned to limbo for sins which he has never committed, but which he might conceivably have committed had he lived.

Under our present system of education, the usual outcome of this struggle is that both the offending drives and the ethical conflicts over them, become buried in such a way as to become inaccessible to conscious self-examination. It is this process of pushing ethical conflicts into the dynamically charged unconscious which is called *repression*. And it is this type of control which does harm, because it is imperfect control. Unaided, the infant or child cannot resolve these ethical conflicts. He hardly knows that they exist. Consequently, unless the child is helped to face his conflicts openly, he automatically buries them where they will persist unrecognized throughout his life, giving rise to many disturbing secondary drives. Furthermore, because the sources of the latter have become unconscious, he will have lost his ability to control and guide them, or to make them conform to his conscious moral ideals. Thus out of the repressed and unconscious residues of ethical conflicts, both neurotic symptoms and immoral conduct arise, sometimes in an individual who may be wholly devoid of conscious evil intent. Actually, the very fact that both the drives and the conflicts over them become unconscious is prima facie evidence of the fact that the child has been engaged in an ethical struggle.

Thus psychoanalysis recognizes that early in the unconscious mental life of the infant and child, forces of "original sin" battle with forces of "original virtue", and that this struggle continues throughout life, most of it being carried on below the level of conscious and articulate awareness. As an unhappy consequence of this, an individual whose ethical needs have forced him to repress his primitive drives may in turn be forced by the repressed residues of those conflicts to act automatically against the very conscience which buried them. This is one reason why destructive people are so rarely men of ill-will or evil purpose.* And this is why so many of us are driven to wrong-doing by forces within ourselves of whose

---

* Kubie, L. S., and Kubie, R. H.: "Destructive Personalities", *Journal of Applied Anthropology*, vol. VII, 4, pp. 36–40, Fall 1948.

existence we are unaware, forces which operate even in the face of an exacting conscience. As a consequence of these considerations, analysis stresses a guiding principle which criminal law has also come to recognize, namely that the boundaries of conscious insight mark the boundaries of moral responsibility. Analysis, however, does not thereby lessen the actual extent of the domain of moral responsibility, since it gives us at the same time a tool which in its ultimate effects broadens this domain by providing us with a method by which man can bring the full light of conscious insight to bear on his unconscious conflicts, thereby giving him the opportunity to deal with them effectively. Thus, in spite of the fact that *repression* operates largely at the instigation of ethical feelings, in its ultimate effects it is a force for evil in human life, since it drives amoral forces underground where they remain powerful and out of reach of voluntary control.

Why the Analyst Never Moralizes

The fact that the effectiveness of responsibility depends in part upon insight into causal forces plays a practical role in the course of every therapeutic analysis. It is quite true that the analyst never "moralizes"; but for this there are several simple reasons. In the first place he wants the patient to develop his own conscience, and not a borrowed facsimile of the analyst's. Secondly, he knows that his patients have heard plenty of moralizing all through their lives, from infancy on. The analyst may be quite certain, therefore, that if moral exhortation could have been effective it would have done its job long before the patient ever came to him for help. Furthermore, if the analyst were to moralize, in the patient's unconscious processes he would at once be identified with those individuals out of the patient's past whose moral authority the patient had long since rejected. Equally automatically, this tendency to reject adult authority would be transplanted into the analysis, so that any naive efforts at moral indoctrination on the part of an analyst would of neces-

sity be spurned. Therefore, the most fundamental task of the
analyst is to give the patient insight into the unconscious
sources of his anti-social behavior, without injecting any
moral judgments into the picture. It should be emphasized,
however, that this elimination of moral judgment is a specific
element in therapeutic technique, and has nothing to do with
the processes of education, or with the nature of the moral
values of analysis or of analysts.

In the early phases of an analysis, the effort to give insight
is limited to retrospective insight into past errors. There is
again a simple reason for this: it is easier for the patient to
face pasᴗ errors than current ones. Later in the analysis the
patient begins to acquire prospective insight, i.e., insight
before action. It is this insight-before-the-act which is the
basis of mature responsibility, because full knowledge of
one's motives before committing oneself to any course of
action requires that we give up the illusory "freedom" to act
impulsively, which is the earmark of immaturity and of bond-
age to one's unconscious.

The analyst sometimes epitomizes this for a patient by
reminding him that the chain of events which leads to our
mistakes begins so early in life, so long before it is reasonable to hold the child responsible, that no one is really responsible for getting into trouble. Every man is responsible,
however, for getting out of it again; and this responsibility
includes an obligation to learn enough about himself to make
it possible to keep out of trouble in the future.

The Fifth Freedom: to Think and Feel without Fear and Guilt

Even within the area of conscious insights, however, analysis makes a distinction between the moral values it places on
actions on the one hand, and on thoughts and feelings on the
other, by hesitating to pass moral judgments on processes as
automatic as the latter. Self-deception concerning thoughts
and feelings is a first step towards repression. Consequently,

analysis recognizes that to tell a child, or for that matter an adult, that his *thoughts or feelings* are wicked can be a first step in the production of either delinquency or neurosis. To the child such an accusation implies that if he were a "good" child he would have no ideas or feelings which were "not nice", and that in some mysterious way his "goodness" would control the free play of his own psychological associations and their accompanying feelings. When we demand that thoughts and feelings should not follow freely their own natural laws, the child becomes both rebellious at the imposition of so unfair and impossible a task, and equally guilty and fear-ridden. It is this demand for the impossible which is the starting point for the split into conscious and unconscious streams of psychological processes, out of which evolve the neurotic process and delinquency (cf. Chapters II and III). Moreover, at times the futile attempt to control thoughts and feelings can make a child fearful that there is something wrong with his very mind. Consequently, the universal fear of insanity has one of its roots in this imposition of an unfulfillable task.

In this respect, psychoanalysis has been a liberating influence in the continuous stream of cultural evolution. Primitive man felt that thoughts were magical and could work evil or do good directly. Man, therefore, had to be held as responsible for his thoughts and feelings as for his actions. For instance, the Ten Commandments forbid us to covet, and the Bible warns that "he who looketh after a woman committeth adultery in his heart." The Godhead is thus invoked as a super-psychological force to strengthen the good in man, either by making him pure enough to be free of all amoral impulses, or else strong enough to control and suppress even their spontaneous psychological representation in thoughts and feelings.

Psychoanalysis faces this problem with different weapons. Man's spontaneous thoughts and feelings are viewed as independent of moral evaluations, since in and of themselves they do not work harm, not on the thinker nor on anyone towards whom they are directed. Neither hate, nor envy, nor lust can do damage unless they are given some form of expression. If they are consciously recognized, acknowledged and understood, then they can be controlled and limited in their expression, and even directed into constructive channels. If on the other hand they are buried and are rendered unconscious, they will express themselves in masked forms, which become automatic, obsessively repetitive, and destructive. Obsession with amoral fantasies and feelings is no more acceptable to the analyst than to the strictest moralist; but this is not because the analyst condemns such an obsession as a sign of immorality, but because he recognizes in it a symptom of illness. An elderly clergyman who had led a blameless life came for help because he had been tortured for years by sudden involuntary eruptions of obscene thoughts during religious services, and by thoughts of irreverent puns and witticisms at funerals. This was a problem in health, not in morals, and was only a compulsively exaggerated version of something that occurs in minor degrees in every child and adult.

For psychoanalysis, moral responsibility implies the validity of the ancient maxim to "know thyself", with the added implication that this must mean self-knowledge in depth. This knowledge must penetrate the barrier between conscious and unconscious levels of the personality, since this is necessary for any effective self-control and self-direction, without which responsibility is an empty concept. The right to self-knowledge in depth becomes man's Fifth Freedom, upon which all other Freedoms ultimately depend.

The Relation of Moral Responsibility to Compulsions

The psychoanalytic concept concerning the conditions under which it is legitimate to hold a man morally responsible requires one further specification. As we have said, psychoanalysts hold that man can reasonably be held responsible only for those aspects of his personality of whose major purposes he is conscious. In addition, it is reasonable to hold him accountable only where the possibility of control exists. Clinical experience demonstrates the practical value of this point. As was pointed out in Chapter III, whenever conduct is determined predominantly by conscious psychological forces, it can respond to moral and spiritual exhortation, to instruction, to rewards and punishments. In short, it can learn from experience. On the other hand conduct which is determined in major part by unconscious forces is precisely to that extent unalterable by external influences, and remains rigidly inflexible until the unconscious forces are brought into the full light of conscious awareness. To hold people responsible for conduct which is determined by compulsive, or as the law says, "irresistible" forces, is both futile and actually destructive.

Therefore, in certain situations moral responsibility even for actions must be qualified. There is a difference between the responsibility of a man who washes his hands when they are dirty, and the man who washes his hands a thousand times a day because he has a hand-washing compulsion. There is a difference between the responsibility of an individual who steals because he wants to make money easily, and of an individual who steals things he does not need and is not going to use or sell, under the internal pressure of a compulsive drive the nature of which he himself does not understand. Subtler and more elaborate compulsive patterns affect many aspects of human life, and in any precise application of the principle of responsibility they must be kept in mind. Where making people feel responsible can help to make their conduct more ethical, the principle of responsibility is valuable both socially and individually. When, however, we try to make anyone feel responsible for something over which he actually has no possibility of control, we merely add a sense of guilt to the complexity of his internal problems, and usually generate rebellious defiance. In fact, there is no surer way to produce delinquents than to give youngsters a sense of shame for conduct over which they have no voluntary control. There is no value in trying to make a child feel responsible for the spots in his measles; yet, to make a child feel guilty about a compulsion amounts to the same thing.

It is not possible to offer any simple rule by which one can be guided in the application of this basic principle. In general, however, (as is explained in detail in Chapters III and IV) the distinction hinges on certain simple pragmatic tests of the modifiability of behavior by external experiences, sensible rewards and moderate punishments, arguments, reason, exhortation and appeals to personal loyalties. Where behavior is resistant to the persistent use of such common-sense influences as these, we may be sure that it is determined predominantly by unconscious forces. Here we are morally responsible chiefly to attempt to understand the nature of the unconscious forces which determine our behavior.

Psychoanalysis and the Concept of Altruism

No one will deny that there are actions which aid others, and actions which injure; actions which give and actions which take. If altruism could be defined pragmatically on the basis of the effects of behavior, any pseudo-philosophic quandary about the existence of altruism would be resolved readily. On the other hand, if its definition must depend on the nature of the psychological processes which determine behavior, the question becomes at the same time extremely complicated and of uncertain significance.

Thus, it is clearly impossible to make any evaluation of motives solely from the effects of behavior either upon others or upon ourselves. The forces which produce behavior are by their very nature complex, multiple, and mutually contradictory. Human behavior is never the product of a single impulse, conscious or unconscious. Everything we do represents the confluence of many streams, or better still, the algebraic summation of many opposing forces. In these congeries of conscious and unconscious impulses one will find love and hate, fear and rage, impulses to dominate and impulses to submit, impulses to give and impulses to grab. How can we call this unstable equilibrium of giving and taking either altruistic or selfish, when from the point of view of motivation it is, and always must be both?

Yet it is in the nature of man that his behavior must serve his needs. Otherwise, in the long run, he could not survive. Therefore, the source of the energies which drive the machine must be ego-centered. Once launched, however, these forces are guided by many other conflicting considerations, much as a push-ball is forced now in one direction and now in another as one team or another gains a temporary ascendancy. In a similar fashion, within any individual, impulses to take at the expense of others and impulses to give at one's own expense are in a continuous unstable equilibrium, now one predominating and now the other. In some individuals, victory will more frequently be on the side of grabbing, in others more often on the side of giving; but in no individual is it exclusively one or the other. And in the end, to survive both physically and spiritually, gratification must outweigh deprivation. Where this is not the case, sickness is bound to result.

From the point of view of the world it is important only that most men should be so educated that their ego-needs will be gratified in part through the service they give to the needs of others.

To the analyst, therefore, altruism and generosity are forms of behavior to which man can be educated, because they meet each man's long-run needs. But to ask that behavior should not in the ultimate analysis be ego-determined is asking water to run uphill, tissues not to require oxygen or water, the body not to need food. It is a fundamental law of life that a man's actions must serve his own needs. But it is an equally fundamental law of society that the service of the needs of the individual and the service of the needs of the group must be harmonized. As long as conscious generosity can screen unconscious selfishness, and vice versa, the ancient philosophical issue of selfishness vs. unselfishness will remain a battle of words.

Psychoanalysis and the Growth of Conscience

A third contribution of psychoanalysis to the concept of moral responsibility focuses on the question of how we learn to be moral. Ultimately, the greatest contribution of psychoanalysis to man's pursuit of the good life may be made in this area. Psychoanalytic studies have shown that automatic patterns of moral behavior are developed not out of the theoretical and philosophical systems with which we rationalize ethical living, nor out of theological attitudes and beliefs, nor in response to ethical exhortations, but rather out of the deeply buried residues of our earliest emotional relationships to our parents or to other important figures. As a consequence of this, the child even of a socially amoral person may develop firm and unshakable ethical patterns, if towards the child that parent is gentle, kind, consistently rewarding and consistently present. The adult may have taught this child no ethics and no religion, and he himself may have practiced none towards the world at large; yet out of the quality of the emotional relationship between the parent and the child, an ethical adult may develop. Conversely, as is well known, a child of ethical and religious leaders, of parents of the highest degree of social integrity and responsibility, may turn out a criminal. This is not because he has failed to learn *about* religion and morality from his parents, but rather because of some morally destructive component in the relationship between the generations. It is what we are towards our children in the nursery, and not what we preach to them, which make them good or bad, because ultimately what they feel towards us unconsciously will determine automatically how they feel unconsciously towards others. It is the quality of these feelings rather than faiths or philosophical systems which in the end determines the ethical level of our lives.

Does this mean that our cultural, ethical, and religious training is bankrupt and impotent, that they have failed? This question plagues every honest and thoughtful educator, every honest and humble minister of every faith, especially at this juncture in the history of mankind, when there is such grave danger that man may destroy himself.

It is no answer to this question to dismiss it by saying, "No, it is *man* who has failed." This is just buck passing, a defense *in a vacuum*. The goal of all educational, religious and cultural processes must be to see to it that man does not fail; and if after thousands of years of effort, man's primitive and destructive drives still remain unaltered in the unconscious depths of his personality, then it is not enough either to bemoan the impotence of cultural influences or to challenge man accusingly. One can say only that to old techniques of human salvation must be added new techniques which can bring out into the open the unconscious aspects of the personality which are the causes of this failure. Blaming is useless, whether it is blaming culture, or religion, or the human being. When an airplane crashes, one saves more lives by learning to understand the laws of gravity than by blaming them. Similarly, the psychoanalyst feels that instead of more exhortation, it is the task of culture and of religion to learn enough about man and his nature to be able to bring his unconscious primitive struggles into closer harmony with his conscious ethical aspirations. Conscious good intentions are still the pavements of hell; and conscious good will is not enough, as long as it so often remains a screen for unconscious ill will. This is precisely where psychoanalysis enters the picture. It will play its historic role in the drama of human development by helping man to bring into the light those unconscious conflicts which hamper his conscious pursuit of the good life. It can hope ultimately to serve the good life even more effectively by helping us to learn how to bring up our children so that they will not have to spend their lives struggling with the bitter unconscious residues of the ethical conflicts of childhood.

Chapter XIX

PSYCHOANALYSIS AND MARRIAGE

The Goal and the Problem

To the *solution* of marital problems, psychoanalysis can sometimes make a significant contribution by uncovering sources of unconscious hostility, guilt and fear, and by clarifying their disguised influences in the marriage. In this way analysis can often lessen or even eliminate their destructive effects. To the *prevention* of marital unhappiness psychoanalysis may well be able someday to contribute a great deal; but only after young folk will have learned that they can never marry themselves out of their neuroses, and that whenever two unhappy young people marry, each adds the problems of his own neurosis to those of the other. From these experiences comes the hard but inescapable conclusion that we must earn our right to marry by solving our individual problems first.

Successful psychoanalytic help for a sick marriage frequently requires the conjoint action of the husband and the wife. All too often, however, before they reach the analyst's office the hostility has become too great for any such mutual effort. The situation is ideal where both come for help, but this is still the exception. More often one or the other comes secretly, or in fear, or in defiance of the other's wishes. Frequently, patients come to an analyst in a state of concealed panic, without having the slightest idea that their marriages are threatened. Unaware of what they are doing, they may try to strike a bargain with the psychoanalyst: "You may analyze me, if you will promise not to uncover any trouble in my marriage." Or they may come with an opposite purpose, trying to blame their own neurotic unhappiness on the marriage, and seeking a pseudo-psychiatric, pseudo-psychoanalytic justification for promiscuity or divorce.

At times, someone comes to seek help in a crisis caused largely by the illness of a husband or wife who refuses to acknowledge either the illness itself, or any need for treatment. The partner's symptoms may be as obvious as chronic alcoholism, impotence, frank sexual perversions, or sadistic compulsive states; yet he may still refuse to acknowledge his need for help. The partner who comes for advice may have shielded the other for years, so successfully indeed, that not even their most intimate friends or relatives have been aware of any difficulty, until the increasing strain and the incessant threat to the welfare of the children finally compels action. In such situations it is not unusual for the healthier of the pair to ask to be analyzed, hoping that by some trick of super-adaptation, some magic of absent treatment, the sick one may be cured without ever submitting to therapy.

Some patients come for analysis resentfully and only under the threat of impending divorce or separation; while others may seek help earnestly, but in the face of bitter resentment and neurotic jealousy on the part of the wife or husband.

These are some of the many and varied snarls which the analyst must untangle before he can decide which one of the partners most needs analysis, and which one, if either, can be analyzed. Sometimes when confronted with a marriage crisis it is hard for the analyst to decide whether or not to undertake an analysis at all, since no matter how successful the analysis may be for the one who accepts his own need for treatment, the outcome of the marriage will depend at least in part upon the ultimate attitude of the unanalyzed partner as well as upon that of the patient. Healthy adaptations can never come exclusively from one side.

It is evident, therefore, that marital problems frequently confront the analyst with difficult decisions. He knows that until a neurosis has hurt a patient there is little hope of his seeking therapy. We do not ask to be treated for those of our neurotic traits which hurt someone else while leaving us relatively unscathed. Indeed, where a neurosis expresses itself by causing pain in a marriage, the greater the pain it causes the more obstinate may be the self-justifying defenses which the potential patient will erect. Frequently, therefore, when an analyst faces a severely threatened and distorted marriage he may have to clear the air both for himself and for his patient by insisting upon a temporary separation before undertaking the analysis. Such a separation, when undertaken for purely technical reasons, can greatly facilitate the progress of an analysis, and may actually save a marriage. On the other hand, this cannot always be the outcome. Sometimes the separation makes it possible for each partner to turn his back on his own contributions to the unhappiness of the marriage. Thus the analyst is in something of a dilemma. On the one hand, if the couple remains together, the constant interplay of mutual hostility between the married pair is likely to swamp the analysis. On the other hand, separation may bring to each a false peace, in which the impulse to search into himself may be completely eliminated. It is impossible for the analyst to be all-wise in resolving this problem as he approaches the treatment of either member of such an unhappy marriage. The only thing he can do is try to maintain a *status quo* until he becomes aware of the more important of the unconscious forces which play below the surface.

Occasionally, however, even in situations which at the outset look hopeless, the gradual improvement of one of the partners may lessen the opposition of the other until he finally seeks help for himself as well. If the children have been psychologically injured in the family battle, they too may ultimately need treatment. This spread of psychoanalysis through a family often arouses cynical comments from onlookers. Nevertheless, to many a family this has meant the difference between happiness and divorce, between disturbed children and their harmonious growth and development.

It must be remembered, however, that psychoanalysis is a medical therapy, and as such must aim primarily at the preservation or restoration of mental and emotional health. The psychoanalyst is not a marriage broker, nor a marriage saver, nor yet a marriage wrecker. Whenever he faces a choice between health or marriage, his medical duty is at least to present this issue clearly, so that the patient can make his choice in the full awareness of its implications. Happily, such an impasse arises less frequently than is popularly believed.

Psychoanalysis and Divorce

People in general have an exaggerated impression of the frequency with which psychoanalysis ends in divorce. Marital conflicts, like other neurotic symptoms, are usually hidden as long as possible. As a result, although the cauldron may have been boiling long before it was brought to the psychoanalyst to be cooled off, no one except the husband and wife may have any suspicion of the extent of the maladjustment. And when the couple finally turns to analysis, the breach may have become too wide for successful analytic intervention. This is one of the reasons for the impression that analysis regularly ends in the disruption of a marriage. Another reason for this impression is that when the analysis succeeds in resolving marital difficulties, no one may have known either that the marriage had been threatened or even that the husband or wife had undergone treatment. Therefore one hears gossip about the analyses which end in divorce, but not about the successful analytic efforts to avert divorce. Divorce has the greater news value.

On the other hand it is true, of course, that divorce sometimes is inevitable. This may be due to any of several reasons: (a) Before the problems were brought to a psychoanalyst, the relationship between husband and wife may have been strained for so many years that even the restoration of health may not be enough to free the patients of their bitterness. Divorce may then be chosen in the end, despite the successful analysis of the neuroses which had destroyed the marriage. (b) Furthermore, many marriages are contracted not on a basis of health, but on that of neurotic purposes. The story is all too familiar of maladjusted young people who try to escape their separate miseries by joining their problems in marriage. Since marriage never cures a neurosis, it usually ends up by being blamed for it; and presently the neurotic angers of both partners are pitted against each other in a merciless battle. Even if this battle can be checked by analysis, the couple may find that with the elimination of the original neurotic reasons for the marriage, no healthy reason remains for continuing together. In such situations separation may be the only healthy solution.

Therefore divorce cannot be used as an index of either the success or failure of an analysis. To do so would be tantamount to claiming that the function of psychoanalysis is not primarily to cure people of their neuroses but to enable them to put up with all the neurotic mistakes they have ever made. The psychoanalyst aims to save a marriage wherever this is humanly possible; the frequency of his success bears testimony both to his purpose and to his ability. Where, however, he must choose between a patient's health and a patient's marriage, this issue must be squarely faced. One cannot leave this topic without looking into the future and asking what would be the effect upon marital happiness and stability if young people had an opportunity to resolve their neuroses before they contracted neurotic alliances. This is a question for the coming decades to answer.

Technical Problems

Of the technical problems which arise in the psychoanalytic treatment of marital difficulties, only two require elucidation here. The first is the problem of the concurrent analysis of husband and wife. This may be of great value when the two analyses are conducted independently by two psycho-analysts; but experienced psychoanalysts generally regard as unwise the simultaneous treatment of both husband and wife by one analyst. This makes no difficulty for the analyst; but, contrary to usual expectations, it makes the task of both patients harder. In the end one or the other is likely to lose his confidence in the impartiality of the analyst; and the analysis of this patient will suffer accordingly. Therefore, since it is usually wise not to postpone the analysis of one until after the other is finished, it is well to send the second patient to another psychoanalyst as soon as possible (cf. Chapters X, XI and XII).

On the other hand, in the preparatory ante-chamber to the analysis, or in cases of marital maladjustment which are not to be psychoanalyzed, both patients can sometimes be handled effectively by the same physician. Yet even here, if the currents of hostile feeling run strong, it may be advantageous to seek the help of two physicians instead of one.

In the analysis of marital problems, one other technical problem is of practical importance to others than psycho-analysts, namely the problem that arises whenever a patient has to work out both a severe personal neurotic problem and a complicated marital conflict. In such circumstances it may be extremely difficult to make headway without separating the two problems. In order to do this, it sometimes is necessary to arrange for a temporary separation, so that the individual's neurotic difficulties can be clarified in some measure before tackling the problems of mutual adjustment. Furthermore in any analysis there may be periods during which neurotic rage is stirred up; and it is almost inevitable that this rage will be vented on the marital partner. Therefore a technical separation during part of an analysis may spare a marriage stresses and strains which might otherwise do final and irreparable damage to it.

Chapter XX

PSYCHOANALYSIS IN RELATION TO SOCIAL, ECONOMIC AND POLITICAL CHANGE

"The Truth Shall Make You Free," *John,* ch. 8, verse 32.

To begin with a disclaimer may seem defensive; yet there is so much misunderstanding and misinterpretation about this topic that it is necessary to dispose of the misconceptions before one can discuss profitably the potential contributions of psychoanalysis to the evaluation of the forms and structure of human society.

In the first place psychoanalysis is not a philosophy of passive submission to the status quo. Its therapeutic goal is not to enable people to put up with the imperfections of our social organization. The analytic ideal of adjustment is rather to enable a man both to acknowledge his own suffering and to identify with that of others, yet without becoming obsessively preoccupied with pain alone. At the same time it aims to give him courage and clarity in his efforts to correct those defects of society which exist all around us and which create suffering. For reasons which will be discussed below, this clarity must include an understanding of many subtle unconscious forces.

In the second place, psychoanalysts as a group adhere to no one political or social or economic philosophy. The most one can say is that like other intellectuals they are thoughtfully concerned with social issues, yet aware of their complexity and of the limitations of their own technical knowledge in these fields. Politically, most analysts are liberal in their sympathies, some tending more to the left and others more to the right largely on the basis of temperamental differences. In his approach to social issues, the only attitude which sets the analyst apart from other intellectuals is a

174

wary search for the influence of unconscious forces, which can warp man's judgments on social as on other problems, inflating the passion of his convictions and determining the methods which he chooses. Because of his suspicion of violence, the analyst is rarely extreme about social issues. He is rarely blindly reactionary, nor impatiently revolutionary. Let us repeat that nevertheless his goal both for himself and for his patients is not to be a fence-sitter, but to achieve freedom for dynamic and effective action, freedom which comes from a clear understanding of the role of unconscious processes in human judgments about all external issues.

It is not an accident, however, that so many contradictory accusations are made about the role of analysis and of the analyst in social issues. All extremists tend to be afraid of analysis. Reactionaries, whether in politics or in religion, call it a radical influence. Radicals call it reactionary; both sides advancing arguments which are full of internal contradictions. For instance, some critics of analysis claim that all neuroses are due to idleness, a mere luxury of the leisure class. Some even go so far as to state that if wealth, economic inequity and the profit motive were eliminated all neuroses would automatically disappear. Yet in the next breath the same critics will assert that neuroses are due not to idleness and wealth but to poverty and want and external insecurity and overwork, failing to realize that the two statements are mutually so contradictory as to nullify each other. Both cannot be true. Nevertheless, a man may make both accusations, because they express his preconceived hope and faith that economic and political reforms can cure all human suffering.

The analyst points out that none of the assumptions which underlie any such conclusion is true. In the first place identical neuroses are found in approximately the same incidence up and down the entire social scale, in all economic classes, in the city and in the country, in highly sophisticated urban circles and on the frontiers of society. Statistical inquiries into the incidence of neurotic difficulties in draftees demonstrated only one clear social factor, namely that among draftees the largest number of rejections for neuropsychiatric disabilities came from those urban districts where the population density was highest.

Clinical experience, therefore, forces the analyst to reject the over-simplified hypothesis that the neurotic process is due to economic inequity. This does not mean, however, that the analyst is complacent about poverty. Here again, not all analysts are cut from the same cloth. They bring to their profession as wide a range of political and economic leanings as is found among lawyers, stockbrokers, school teachers, clergymen, chemists, engineers, and housewives. Furthermore, there are some who concern themselves exclusively with scientific problems. This is entirely legitimate, since some men can make their greatest contributions to human welfare by an exclusive absorption in science. Except for the fact that analysts practice all day and teach all night (cf. Chapter XXII), and consequently have little time for other interests, there is nothing in analysis as such which would force all analysts either into a scientific ivory tower or into the market-place. Like other scientific disciplines, analysis allows the individual analyst freedom to express his social and political interests in his own way.

There is one further reason, however, for the persistent notion that analysts isolate themselves from the economic, social and political problems of the world around them. However deeply concerned about such issues an analyst may be, he soon finds that once he begins to devote much time and attention to such issues, he is in danger of short-changing his patients. At first this will be negligible in its effects; but as time goes on their analyses suffer seriously. More important than the time and energy which extra-analytic activities absorb, is the shift of the analyst's own interest and feeling from the exacting work of analyzing to the emotionally less taxing and somewhat more spectacular field of social reform.

It is like looking up from a microscope to admire a view. For an analyst with a conscience, a good fight in a worthy cause is a powerful magnet, luring his attention from the subtler task of analysis; but any analyst who has checked himself closely must admit that during periods in which he has become involved in worthy non-analytical activities he has found it more difficult to keep his attention focused on his patients sufficiently to enable his own thoughts to play spontaneously, freely, and imaginatively with the patient's material.

Analysis is a lonely task, and one which requires of the analyst that all of his conscious and unconscious angers must be drained off into channels which will not endanger the analysis. Social and political reforms, or fights about the organization of analytic education and about analytic theory or technique, drain off these angers and lessen the analyst's loneliness. This is on the credit side. On the debit side, however, there is the danger of draining off the creative as well as the destructive energies of the analyst from the work of analyzing. That is why some analysts say half-jokingly that in order to do the finest analytic work that is humanly possible, the analyst would have to live in a monastery on top of a mountain.

Evidently in this matter the analyst faces a dilemma. On the one hand, if all analysts were to retreat into isolation, analysis as such would lose much of its social value and cultural significance. On the other hand active participation in social problems jeopardizes in some measure the individual analyst's value to the patients for whose treatment he has assumed a deep moral responsibility. Therefore, before he undertakes any activity outside of his analytical work, he must satisfy his conscience: (a) that this activity is so essential that he is justified in allowing it to break into his analytic schedule; and (b) that he is the only person, or the best person or the essential person to do that particular task.

It is important for society and for analysts themselves to be clear about this; because as analysis grows in popularity, the counsel and advice of analysts are sought on public issues, and their participation is valued in many communal activities. Some analysts are particularly gifted and effective in such work, and consequently are likely to be drawn into many worthy "causes". The more successful they are, the stronger is the pressure on them to take on more and more such activities. The analyst who has yielded to this seduction tends to turn away from analysis. He may then rationalize this by belittling the importance of analytic work with the individual patient, forgetting that this has been and will continue to be the source of everything analysts can contribute to an understanding of public affairs. Under these circumstances, there is some danger that the patient would become the forgotten man of analysis. How psychoanalysts will ultimately resolve this dilemma is not yet clear. We may be sure that the same individual cannot perform both functions, except at the expense of his patients. On the other hand, if one group of analysts sticks to the clinical grindstone and another group gambols over the fields of social reform, mutual distrust and suspicion is likely to arise between the two groups. The clinicians may turn their backs on world forces; while the reformers are likely to lose contact with the subtle complexities of the clinic, and in their efforts to make psychoanalytic knowledge more immediately acceptable and applicable they may over-simplify it and dilute it until it becomes both banal and ineffectual. The contributions which psychoanalysts can make to social problems are so great that some solution for this dilemma must, nevertheless, be found. We must watch carefully, however, to make sure that in expanding into the social fields we do not sacrifice either technical precision, or theoretical clarity about the individual human being and his unconscious, and about the interrelationship of his conscious and unconscious processes. Without technical precision and without theoretical clarity psychoanalysis would have nothing to offer to human progress.

A more specific accusation, i.e., that the analyst is unconcerned with the welfare of the poor, arises in part from those anomalies in the economics of analytic practice, which are discussed in detail in Chapter XVI, and which will be recapitulated here briefly. Because his training takes so long the analyst can rarely start earning a living until well on in years. By this time he is usually close to forty, with a family to support. Therefore, few years are left in which to earn an education for his children and some measure of security for his own old age. Furthermore, he can never take care of more than a few patients at a time. Consequently, under our economic system he cannot afford to treat many patients free of charge. Most analysts teach without remuneration, and also treat a few patients gratis, or for a token payment; but the total number of such patients cannot be large. This gives rise to the wholly erroneous impression that the analyst deals only with the wealthy, which leads to the further assumption that his social and economic attitudes will be colored by this hypothetical clientele. None of this is true; but even if it were, it would concern only the facts of psychoanalytic practice in our present economic system, and it would have nothing to do with the bearing of psychoanalytic theory on economic and social reform.

The spirit of scientific skepticism and inquiry which psychoanalysis brings to bear on the human spirit also has something to do with the suspiciousness with which both sides of the political fence view analysis. Actually neither side wants its own unconscious motives examined; but the analyst is equally suspicious of the drive to maintain the status quo and of the drive to change everything. The analyst deals constantly with the disguised derivatives of the primitive and unconscious cruelty which is hidden behind our civilized mask; and his respect for the power of unconscious conflicts makes him fearful of irresponsible power, even in the hands of consciously well-meaning people. Therefore he is acutely aware of how essential it is to limit and restrict power, to hold responsible those who wield it, and to buffer people against its direct manifestations; and he fears above all else any struggle for naked and irresponsible power, whether in industry or in government.

Naturally this influences profoundly his attitude both to economic and political forms, and to the processes of change. For instance, while they recognize the evils that arise when too much wealth puts great power in the hands of the few, some analysts are impressed by the fact that the power to cause suffering which money wields is more often indirect than direct. It can overwork, and it can cause sickness, starvation and even death by underpayment; but it does not produce a Dachau or a Belsen. With all its evils, money also serves in certain respects as a buffer which for centuries has protected people from more naked manifestations of the competitive and destructive drives which human beings harbor. Some analysts feel, therefore, that the rivalry for property, for purchasing power, and for display, tends to be less brutally inhuman in its effects than are the primitive rivalries and brutalities of totalitarian power politics. As deeply as anyone else, analysts deplore the abuses of the struggle for money; but since the neurotic process starts long before the infant deals with any medium of exchange, few analysts regard money as a causal factor in the origin of the neurotic process. That money can influence its evolution and become one of its symptomatic expressions is obvious. Many analysts wonder, however, whether the human race will be ready to do without this shock absorber of human aggressions, until it has learned to resolve in early childhood the angry struggles which are the unconscious and insatiable origins of adult rivalry and envy.

Analysts vary widely in their convictions on all such issues as these, some standing far to the right and some equally far to the left, and some in the middle of the road. What is important is the fact that these are not issues about which psychoanalysis *per se* demands any single conviction. It is important for the layman, whatever his political persuasion, to be clear about this; because among some of the more naive followers of Horney there has been a revolt against the Freudian concept of the biological basis of neurotic behavior, which parallels closely the recent Russian revolt against certain basic elements in the concept of heredity. Just as the Russian political ideology rejected heredity because it seemed to them to limit the power of economic reform to cure all human ills, so these "analysts" reject biogenetic factors, because they want to attribute to economic forces a curative power which can overcome any disturbing psychological force. Out of this bias they have brewed an intellectually incompetent and indigestible mixture of reactionary science and economic radicalism. They have used this, in turn, as a platform from which to attack Freudian psychoanalysis, as though the latter stood for accepting the *status quo* supinely and at any cost, which is demonstrably untrue. As we have said, the goal of analysis is to develop a maximum degree of conscious dynamic adaptability and flexibility in every individual, while creating and preserving an active need to eliminate the abuses in human life, coupled with clarity both about the reforming drive and about the abuses which demand reform.

The accusation that the goal of adjustment is to make human beings submit meekly to all of the inequities and abuses of life has a familiar ring. We have heard it often in the past, in connection with every effort to help man to adjust to the realities of life. For instance it has often been leveled at religion. It is true of course that in the history of the world religion has frequently been exploited for this purpose by vested interests. Yet many deeply religious people have been revolutionary in their attitude toward economic, social and political wrongs; which proves that the passive and uncomplaining acceptance of evil is certainly not an essential part of religion. The accusation is equally invalid when it is leveled against the essential goal and purpose of psychoanalysis.

In clarifying this misunderstanding it may be helpful to consider one further reason why these accusations are made. It is to be found in the psychology of the reformer. Most reformers hope that alterations in the forms and organization of human life will eliminate human misery and discontent. Naturally, such a reformer will resent anyone who points out the complexities of the process of human progress, because an acknowledgment of complexity frustrates the need for simple solutions. Furthermore, just as the stand-patter may be moved by his unconscious anger to exploit and oppress and exclude, so too the need for change at any cost may be driven by a secret rage, which finds a legitimized expression in the reforming impulse. The furious and prurient obscenity of some of the advocates of purity is a well-known and gross example of this; but it is difficult for men of more genuine good will to recognize in their own activities subtler versions of the same paradox. Therefore, insofar as psychoanalysts are chronic skeptics about simple cures for human ills, they dam up the rage which is one of the sources of the zeal of both sides; and this bottled-up rage turns against the skeptical and cautious analysts, taking the form of personal accusations against them and against everything they stand for.

In his approach to social reform, the psychoanalyst is impressed by the many examples of the confused thinking that arises out of the unconscious residues of the early struggle against parental authority. This struggle begins in the small child's impotent struggle against the power and authority of adults, and in his rivalry with other children. In every individual, this gives rise to an internal conflict between impulses to submit and impulses to rebel, a struggle which usually becomes so violent that it has to be repressed. Years later, this hidden conflict reappears, displaced against social institutions or various substitute figures. The man who as a child could not acknowledge his patricidal rage against his own father may rebel with an inappropriate murderous anger against the army, against his foreman or his boss, or against society as a whole. Another may repress the same conflict so deeply that he will submit to anything. Sometimes both of these contradictory components of a child's feelings may be expressed separately in the same adult. Thus one man may accept irresponsible power in his own country without objection, while railing against absolute power in some distant land, i.e., at a safe distance. This is the typical position of some reactionary isolationists. Another man may protest violently against the least flaw in civil or economic liberty at home, but will praise totalitarian power thousands of miles away as though it were a blessing. We saw such inconsistencies in the isolationist who was up in arms against any federalization of power in this country, but was an active admirer of Hitler and Mussolini. We see the same confusion in the fellow-traveler who is indignant at the least infringement of human liberty in America, but finds Russian totalitarianism admirable. In none of these instances would analysis aim to make submissive children out of adult men. It would aim rather to clarify such confusions and to eliminate such paradoxical inconsistencies by enabling men to deal objectively with problems of authority, whether in their own countries or in the distant world, judging these problems on their own merits and without being misled by the unresolved residues of the blind rebellion of their own nursery years. The analyst wants men to seek emancipation with open eyes free from concealed neurotic distortions.

Because the analyst deals every day with the adult manifestations of the residues of childhood fear, hatred, jealousy, and greed, he knows that these infantile emotions occur even when no external deprivation exists. In the most inclusive sense of the word, therefore, the goal of analysis is freedom. By freedom, however, the analyst means freedom from the tyranny of unconscious psychological forces quite as much as freedom from external tyranny. The struggle for external freedom has produced the evolution of political democracy, which now is moving slowly and painfully towards economic democracy. Analysis recognizes the fact that to make democracy work requires emotional as well as intellectual maturity, a maturity which implies freedom from the grip of those unconscious inner forces which are the residues of our infancy and childhood. In the analyst's experience this internal slavery proves to be quite as destructive of human happiness as political and economic slavery can be of human life. Without the other, neither one has taken us very far along the road towards the good life. The analyst knows that one man may be a rebel for sound and healthy reasons and another for neurotic reasons; that one man can be a submissive conformist who complacently blinds himself to social inequity for neurotic reasons, while another accepts such painful realities as a psychologically healthy man will accept the fact of cancer, until a treatment which is hopeful enough to warrant trial becomes available. The psychologically healthy man does not try to cure his cancer with witchcraft, merely to express indignation at his hard fate. The analyst knows, therefore, that in order to succeed, basic changes in the organization of human life must parallel an internal and spiritual evolution. As he strives for this goal with each analytic patient, he views their joint endeavor as part of the great human struggle for freedom.

In the long view, therefore, the analyst is a revolutionary who seeks revolution by evolution, and who resorts to violent revolutionary techniques only reluctantly and as a last resort.

Once he has become convinced, however, that revolution is the only method by which progress can be achieved, he will not flinch from it, although he will take no joy in it.   It is the difference between the soldier who fights well although he hates war and the psychopath who wins Congressional Medals for bravery because combat gives him a legitimate way of expressing his anti-social, amoral destructive impulses.   It is this kind of soldier whose influence the analyst would attempt to eliminate from the battle for social, economic, and political reforms.*

* Those who are particularly interested in this problem can be referred to an article by Judson T. Stone on "The Theory and Practice of Psychoanalysis", which appeared in *Science and Society* in 1946, Vol. 10, No. 1, pp. 54–79. This with a few reservations is an excellent introduction to certain theoretical aspects of the topic, and also to the literature.   Others may be interested in Lenin's caustic criticism of certain types of blind radicalism in *'Left-Wing' Communism, an Infantile Disorder*, V. I. Lenin, The International Publishers, 381 Fourth Avenue, New York 16, N. Y.

Chapter XXI

A RECAPITULATION OF CERTAIN COMMON MISCONCEPTIONS ABOUT PSYCHOANALYSIS

It is natural that a young science should be misunderstood. It passes through periods of conflicting theories. New concepts develop and new terms are coined which overlap with earlier terms and concepts and with one another. Theories are advanced simultaneously in different countries and in different languages, the imperfect translations of which result in confusion over the mere meanings of terms. Gradually, however, as a science comes of age, its language is pruned and its garden of concepts weeded. In psychoanalysis the pruning and weeding has begun.

In time these natural sources of early misunderstanding all yield to clearer thinking and simpler language. Sometimes, however, the misunderstandings persist in spite of all explanations. When this happens it is due not to confusions within the growing science, but to the fact that deeply entrenched biases, both conscious and unconscious, have been challenged. Witness the violent attacks which were made by supposedly learned men against those who first insisted that the world was round rather than flat, and against the discoverers of the theory of evolution. Such attacks are often filled with misrepresentations which are hard to correct. This happened to Darwin, Huxley, Pasteur, and more recently to Freud.

In spite of many careful explanations, psychoanalysis continues to be subjected to gross misrepresentations, almost as though its critics need to make it appear foolish or obscene, want it not to make sense, want it to seem immoral, and therefore never read the many published explanations that could dispel their misconceptions. Striking examples of this have recently been broadcast to the public both from the pulpit and in popular periodicals. Therefore, once again, one sets about the slow task of undoing the mischief.

There are many such misconceptions, of which we will discuss a few.

(1) Does analysis, as opposed to something called "synthesis", destroy the personality?

(2) Does psychoanalysis deliberately cultivate a love relationship between the patient and the analyst through what is called the "transference"?

(3) Does psychoanalysis deny moral responsibility and sanction sin? Connected with this is the question of the relationship of analysis to the confession.

(4) Does psychoanalysis advocate the unlimited pursuit of pleasure and of self-indulgence?

(5) Why is the cost of psychoanalysis high, is it prohibitive, and if so, what can be done about it?

(1) One hears frequently that analysis is a disintegrating experience. To anyone who understands the processes by which neuroses form and by which they are cured, these statements are so naive as to be meaningless. In the psychological apparatus of every human being, sick or well, there is an incessant interplay between synthetic forces and dissociative or disintegrative forces. Neuroses form when the balance moves in the latter direction; and when the balance moves in the former direction the process of healing is at work. This can happen only when disintegrative and dissociative forces are eliminated: but their elimination is precisely the goal and technique of analysis. When this occurs, spontaneous synthetic processes are freed and nature takes care of the rest. The protest that analysis is disruptive is as meaningless as it would be to say to a surgeon who was opening an abscess or removing a tumor that what we need is healing not cutting. Just as health is the goal of medicine but not a technique of treatment, so synthesis is the goal of

psychoanalysis, as it is of all psychotherapy, but not a technique for getting well. In psychological matters as in the tissues, once the causes of dissociation have been removed, synthesis occurs spontaneously. (Cf. Chapters III, IV, and XV.)

(2) A great deal of nonsense has been said and written about what in psychoanalysis is called the "transference", or the "analysis of the transference." Often it is pictured as something which is put over on the unwary victim; as a Machiavellian method by which an analyst artificially induces in a patient a peculiar attachment to himself; as a method reserved for young and beautiful women and never used with the poor or the ugly, or, for that matter, with men; as a highly pleasurable state of infatuation with the analyst; and finally as something which is supposed to develop only at the end of an analysis. For example, one critic recently wrote, "Then one day I learned that at the end of my treatment I was supposed to transfer all the love, faith, and confidence which heretofore I had placed in other beings, human or divine, to the personality of my psychoanalyst."

On every count, these fantasies about transference are wide of the mark. In the first place such credulity destroys an analysis (cf. Chap. XVII). Second, transferred feelings run the whole gamut of human emotions, including hate and fear and distrust and rivalry and envy, quite as much as "love, faith, and confidence." Third, "transference" is not a "method used in psychoanalysis", but a universal phenomenon which occurs in varying measure in every human relationship. Furthermore, this transference of feelings occurs spontaneously and from the start of the treatment, out of preformed patterns of feeling which exist in every patient before he comes for treatment. It need never be cultivated by any analytic artifice. Peculiar to psychoanalysis is only one fact, namely that in analytic therapy the transferred feelings are studied with the patient so as to make clear what part of these feelings are appropriate and what part are inappropriate, and how they have arisen out of pre-existing unconscious fantasies. This is of great value to the patient, because it shows him how such displaced feelings can distort all of his human relationships. Consequently, there is never a psychoanalytic treatment, be it of an old man or of a young woman, of adult or child, of rich or poor, ugly or beautiful, in which transference does not occur, and in which the transference is not analyzed. Several concrete examples to demonstrate this are given in Chapter VIII. In all of those examples it is clear that hostile feelings play quite as important a role as do feelings of affection; or in technical jargon, the negative transference may be quite as important as the positive transference. In fact both negative and positive elements are present in any analysis; although from time to time one may be more evident than the other. Nor do the terms imply that one is useful and the other useless or obstructive. Both are of the utmost value to the analysis, provided only that they are wisely and penetratingly used.

Thus, this process which analysts have called "transference" can make a man treat a business associate as though he were his brother, an employer as though he were his father, a teacher as though she were his mother. It can make us behave in ways which may have been appropriate to childhood, but which are inappropriate to adult years. It is one of several forces which can lead people to hate those against whom they have no grievance, love those for whom they have no valid basis for affection, fear those who are no threat to them. By distorting human relationships it hampers and cripples the universal groping for maturity and for that integrated existence which all men seek. Therefore, for sociologists and cultural anthropologists, and for ethical and religious leaders, as for the psychoanalyst, it is important to understand this universal process and to make others understand its destructive role in human affairs. To learn how thoroughly we can fool ourselves about both our loving and our hating is a humbling lesson which has profound cultural value, assisting frail mankind in its struggle to become civilized.

(3) Another widely held misconception is that psychoanalysis is "an easy way out," a slick device for dodging responsibility for our mistakes, a method of explaining everything away so as to avoid paying the piper. This again is far from true. It is obvious that actual guilt and fantasies of guilt are not identical. Every psychiatrist knows the blameless patient who is haunted by feelings of guilt, and who goes around wringing his hands and saying, "There is something I am guilty of, but I don't know what it is". Every police officer and every priest knows that men give themselves up for crimes they could not possibly have committed. Every juvenile court officer knows how many youngsters actually set out to get caught, so as to be punished for minor crimes, in order to hide their guilt over impulses about which they feel more guilty than about any act. And every analyst knows that many men and women wear masks of innocence while hiding from themselves the most profound and devastating unconscious convictions of sin. It is the job of the analyst to attempt to bring order out of this chaos. This he does by bringing to light the unconscious feelings which may hide behind conscious feelings of either guilt or innocence, and by making it clear how, in some instances, we bribe our consciences into silence, and in others torture and flagellate ourselves with fantastic feelings of guilt. Certainly, there is wisdom in the old saw that an honest confession is good for the soul; but analysis has made us realize how subtle and elusive an honest confession may be, and that confession, like everything else in human life, may be misused for neurotic purposes (cf. Chapter XVIII).

I would like to quote from *Mind, Medicine and Man*, by Gregory Zilboorg:*

* Harcourt, Brace and Company, New York, 1943, p. 328.

"Psychoanalysis is not confession, nor is it like confession. Confession is a conscious act of repentance, and a ritual. Man can confess only that which he consciously knows, that which makes him consciously guilty; as a result of confession and the officially given absolution man feels relieved, and he is admonished and inspired not to sin any more. In psychoanalysis the patient cannot confess in the usual sense of the word. The patient gradually reveals the unconscious sense of guilt of which he has been unaware; he is not given absolution, nor does the psychoanalyst have any means at his disposal to relieve the patient of this guilt. What the psychoanalyst does do is listen and watch how the patient learns, gradually and almost imperceptibly, to differentiate fantasy from reality, infantile from adult impulses. The patient then obtains relief from feeling guilty about things of which he is not guilty at all, and he continues to feel guilty about those things of which one usually does and should feel guilty."

Furthermore, analysis recognizes that from earliest years many streams converge to make us behave as we do, and that many of these streams started at so early an age that we can hardly be said to have been responsible for them, in an adult sense. Consequently, no individual alone and of himself is responsible for landing himself in a mess. Yet the very existence of analysis, as a joint undertaking of a patient and an analyst, is an acknowledgment of the fact that, whether or not we are responsible for getting ourselves into trouble, the responsibility for getting ourselves out of trouble rests with each one of us. This is true ethical responsibility, since it implies that it is our job to repair even those psychological damages which we have not brought upon ourselves. To analysis, payment in kind is not enough. Self-flagellation is not enough. Penance and confession alone are not enough. This is because the sick human being can misuse all such ethical devices and still "sin" again. To these time-honored ways of dealing with the primitive components of human nature, analysis has added an insight into the unconscious as well as the conscious roots of conduct; and it is specifically this insight which gives human beings their first real chance to rise to new levels of emotional and ethical maturity.

Perhaps it is accurate to say that all modern theologies use the feelings of guilt and of anxiety as forces with which the sinner can be led to repent and to turn to faith in a divine mercy. At times every psychiatrist sees patients in whom the resulting burden of guilt and anxiety is inflated to a destructive extent by unconscious fantasies. This is especially true when rigid ethical standards are exacted not merely for acts, but also for thoughts and feelings. The expansion of the ethical code to include responsibility and accountability not merely for one's deeds but also for one's thoughts, feelings, and desires was a momentous step in human culture. Yet it placed an unfair and sometimes crushing burden on the human spirit, because before the discoveries of psychoanalysis nothing was understood of the role of unconscious forces in determining the conscious levels of thought and feeling. Any system of ethics which demands something which is psychologically impossible must inevitably create a pathological anxiety and pathological guilt; and these substitute obsessional struggles over scruples and rituals for normal ethical goals. The outcome of this is to divide men into two groups: neurotic slaves to rigid systems of ethics, and neurotic rebels against them.

Once this is clearly understood, it becomes evident that in a quite specific way psychoanalysis is an essential supplement to the cultural advances of modern religion, by giving us a weapon with which to alter the primitive and savage unconscious levels which form the core of our major ethical struggles.

(4) Another frequent misconception about psychoanalysis is the idea that it advocates an undisciplined pursuit of self-indulgence; or as one critic recently put it, "materialism, hedonism, infantilism, and eroticism". This is especially untrue. Actually, the Freudian concept of the human strug-

gle has its roots in sober and time-tested theological formulations. Like the theologian, the analyst sees man as struggling up from childhood between primitive destructive and erotic instincts on the one hand, and his conscience and his ideal aspirations on the other. Let us recall again that it was none other than St. Augustine who pointed out that the so-called innocence of childhood is due more to the weakness of their limbs than to the purity of their hearts. Furthermore, it was the theologians who propounded the doctrine of Original Sin, which is merely another way of characterizing the primitive components of child nature. What psychoanalysis has added, however, is again the fact that a large part of this struggle takes place below the level of consciousness: and that the unconscious protagonists in this conflict must be mastered as well as the conscious. Out of this psychoanalytic discovery have come the beginnings of a technique, faltering and imperfect though it still is, by which human beings can bring their primitive unconscious drives to the surface where they can be controlled and directed.

It is fair to remind ourselves that before this discovery, man's progress had in fact been blocked for centuries. Even prior to the Christian era man could formulate his goals, and indeed did so, beautifully and movingly, in many religions, in literature, and in the arts. But experience taught that to describe those goals or to seek them with exhortation and prayer failed to bring us much closer to them. As long as they remain hidden, our concealed inner drives continue to force us to live in ways which run counter to our highest aims. Only by the mastery of these buried forces can man win the freedom to attain his ideals. Many have described the shining city at the end of the road. It is the grubby function of the analyst to learn how to roll out of the path the internal boulders which make progress so difficult. This is hardly the picture of the idle, frivolous, hedonistic, pleasure-loving philosophy which is so erroneously attributed to the psychoanalyst.

Nor is it true to say that psychoanalysis advocates unlimited self-indulgence of any kind. Freud, himself a strict and almost ascetic figure in his personal life, never said that the control of instincts was to be abandoned in favor of unbridled pleasure-seeking. Quite on the contrary, he repeatedly described how the pursuit of pleasure (the "pleasure principle") must even in infancy be tempered by the "reality principle". Here again, however, Freud added two discoveries, both of which are often misrepresented: (1) that conscience itself, like the instincts of man, can serve unconscious neurotic processes which we must learn to understand; (2) that whereas conscious mastery and control of instincts leads to health and strength, unconscious suppression (i.e., repression) leads almost regularly to illness. This distinction is so elementary and has been explained so often that it is hard to understand how it can still be misunderstood and misrepresented.

This notion, that analysis advocates the unchecked and self-indulgent expression of every impulse, arises not only from a misunderstanding about the difference between conscious and unconscious control, but also from a failure to realize the difference between therapy on the one hand and education or child training on the other. It is true that for technical reasons in treatment, as a temporary device, one sometimes has to relax many of the ordinary controls. In the early days of psychoanalysis, what was then called "progressive education" made the natural mistake of thinking that this therapeutic device should apply to schools and to the training of children in the home. Therefore, we passed through a somewhat grotesque period in which the so-called modern school or modern home encouraged children in all kinds of unwise extravagances of speech and behavior. Happily, this period has long since passed, but the popular misunderstanding persists.

(5) Finally, what of the frequent accusation that psychoanalysis is only for the wealthy? Even in the pioneering

period which is just ending, many more analyses were performed without charge, or for token payments, than has been realized. Whenever in the history of medicine a new technique has first to be tried out in private practice, it is unavoidable that there will be a period during which its use is limited to a relatively small group among all who need it. During this phase the rich are the proving ground for the poor; and it is only as the new techniques become well established, and as many physicians are trained in their use, that it becomes possible to distribute their benefits widely. Psychoanalysis is at present emerging from this initial phase of predominantly private practice, to one of broader social applications in many fields. The practical problems with which such a program is confronted are described in Chapters XVI and XXII.

In order to place psychoanalytic knowledge at the service of larger segments of the population, it will be necessary to provide funds and an organization for the training of more psychiatrists in psychoanalysis, and various new types of treatment facilities in which psychoanalytic psychiatry can be used: e.g., in outpatient clinics for the treatment of the neuroses; in the treatment of psychosomatic problems in general hospitals; in the rehabilitation of workers in industry; in family counseling; at all levels of schooling; and in courts and social agencies. The number of individuals to be helped is enormous; the number of those who are adequately trained to give such help is pitifully small. This is the bottleneck, and it can be broken only by endowing teachers and students alike. A few years of generous policies in this matter, making use of both private philanthropy and public funds, would be repaid many times over. This is why such organizations as the New York Psychoanalytic Institute and other similar training institutes are now attempting to raise large endowment funds.

Thus, there is good reason to believe that psychoanalysis stands on the threshold of a new era; and that what has been learned during its first fifty years will make wider applications possible both in prevention and in therapy. To reach these goals, however, requires the understanding cooperation of the community in which we live and work, and especially of all those institutions and instruments of popular instruction which form and influence public opinion. That is why from the point of view of the community and its needs it is worthwhile to attempt once more to dispel some of the more frequent misconceptions about analysis.

IV. Training and Organization

Chapter XXII

PSYCHOANALYTIC TRAINING

The Name

There is no copyright on the name "psychoanalyst". Nevertheless it is becoming increasingly difficult for anyone to call himself a psychoanalyst who has not subjected himself to an apprenticeship which is one of the longest and most arduous in medicine. This fact is gradually ridding the field of untrained pretenders.

We may safely conclude, therefore, that it is in the interest of the public and of the medical profession in general to define a psychoanalyst as one who is a member in good standing of any Psychoanalytic Society which, in turn, is affiliated with the American or the International Psychoanalytic Association. Such membership is equivalent to certification as a specialist; and it is a sound medical practice to deny the name of psychoanalyst to anyone who lacks such training. Therefore, it is a useful precaution to find out whether any man who calls himself an analyst belongs to such a society or is sponsored by a training institute (e.g., an advanced student), before accepting him as an adequate representative of a method which he claims to use.

Historical Development of Psychoanalytic Training

When psychoanalysis was young, anyone who was interested could join a psychoanalytic society, whose members met to discuss the new science and to listen to lectures on the subject; and any member could practice something which he called "psychoanalysis". Thereafter, his further growth was determined by his own clinical experience, his study of the writings of others, his inherent gifts, and his integrity. Many able and courageous pioneers grew up under this system: but

197

the going was hard, they faced bitter and scornful criticism, and the material rewards were limited. For many years, therefore, no opportunist was tempted to exploit the new technique.

As the popularity of psychoanalysis grew, however, this informality and this lack of well-defined standards of training led to abuses. Many people began to call themselves psychoanalysts who by no process of self-instruction or self-discipline had achieved any understanding of the principles and methods of what they claimed to practice. There still are a few such men whose methods are at variance with the essence of psychoanalytic technique but who nonetheless are regarded as psychoanalysts by the laity, and even by some members of the medical profession. Some of these were in the field so early that they have been members of some psychoanalytic society for many years; but only a few of them are left. From time to time fresh abuses still occur. Recently, a sign in a window claimed that the man within was a "Chiropractor and Psychoanalyst". Another man boasted that he could "analyze" his patients in an hour. A glib physician, totally without training either in psychiatry or psychoanalysis, talked of "working the transference on" his patients. A woman thought she was being analyzed when she was seeing her physician for half an hour once a week over a period of a few weeks. Fortunately, however, with the diffusion of accurate information, such distortions as these are disappearing.

There remains a more respectable source of confusion which can be stamped out only with the full cooperation and help of the laity and of the medical profession. This is the unwitting misuse of the term "psychoanalysis" by physicians who may be well trained in other fields of medicine or surgery. Every physician is likely to be called upon by his patients to advise them on their emotional problems. Some physicians soon develop an aptitude for this work; and before long the word goes around that they are "analyzing" their patients. The physician may or may not be responsible for this confusion. Sometimes he himself does not understand the difference between analysis and what he is doing. There is no consultant in the field of psychiatry and psychoanalysis who has not had to repair the damage which these well-intended but untrained efforts can cause.

Some of these physicians may sincerely believe that a "flair" for human contacts is the equivalent of training in psychiatry and psychoanalysis, as though a man's manual dexterity were the equivalent of a thorough apprenticeship in surgery. On the basis of an interest in the problems of human nature, they offer the public their personally blended version of psychotherapy, in which some features of psychoanalysis may be included. To analytic colleagues, these men will carefully explain that what they practice is *not* psychoanalysis; but to their patients or in the presence of a more naive group they maintain with equal vigor that it is, and rationalize their lack of training by attacking analytic training as rigid and "orthodox." It is true, of course, that formal training in any field has to guard constantly against rigid traditionalism; but this is hardly a valid excuse for rejecting training *in toto*. Sometimes this is done with naive sincerity; sometimes it is a product of a physician's megalomanic neurosis; sometimes it is flagrant opportunism. But it is well for the medical profession and public to remember that there is no royal road to analytic skill through guess and intuition alone.

Occasionally under the pressure of the difficulties into which they flounder, these medical or surgical colleagues apply to the nearest psychoanalytic Institute for admission as regular students. If they agree sincerely to accept the jurisdiction of the school, to fill in the basic gaps in their psychiatric education, and to put themselves through the further training which is required of all students, such applications are welcome. The sacrifices which this involves are heavy, however, and include the abandonment of the pseudoanalytical practice on which the applicant has probably come to depend for his very living. When they find out how great a sacrifice is involved and how exacting is the discipline, some of these applicants change their minds and fail to start; and of those who start, some fail to finish. Some, however, have completed their belated training, and their courage and integrity have been rewarded by the acquisition of an exceptional skill.

None of these abuses can be controlled by law, but physicians can protect their patients by making sure that any man to whom they wish to refer a patient for analysis is recognized as an analyst through membership in one of the official societies which are affiliated with the American or International Psychoanalytic Societies, or else by training in psychoanalysis at one of the Institutes which are recognized by these organizations.

It has been for the purpose of training competent specialists that Institutes were organized in which to educate those who wish to master this particular branch of medical therapy. The training given by a recognized psychoanalytic Institute constitutes the best evidence of a physician's right to call himself a psychoanalyst and to call what he practices psychoanalysis.

The International Psychoanalytic Society

This training developed first under the supervision of the International Psychoanalytic Association. Before the war this consisted of societies in many lands, whose individual members made up the membership of the international body. The International Psychoanalytic Association was thus a federation of local scientific societies, and membership in it was automatic upon election to the local societies recognized by the international body. Under the guidance of an International Training Commission the local societies organized training institutes. Thereafter no one could be elected to membership in any society who had not graduated from such an institution. All training, therefore, was based on certain general principles laid down by the training commission of the International Society.

In the early days of psychoanalysis this centralized control made it possible for responsible leaders of psychoanalysis to establish and maintain high standards everywhere; but it entailed the risk of becoming too authoritarian and too tradition-bound in theory and technique. Consequently, the organization which was formed to preserve standards led to the splitting-off of some rebellious groups, amid angry accusations that the Training Commission was stifling free scientific thought. This, though a source of confusion to laymen and physicians alike, has been a natural and transitory difficulty. In the main, whatever was valid in these rebellions was absorbed into the theories and techniques of the parent group; and consequently their effect was healthy and stimulating, in spite of any temporary confusion they have caused. Furthermore, with the vigorous scientific development of psychoanalysis and its wide dispersion over the world, the authority of the Central Executive and of the Training Commission of the International Association has lessened steadily, and the whole structure is now in the process of being decentralized.

The American Psychoanalytic Association*

In America for many years there has been an organization known as the American Psychoanalytic Association. During its early years its members varied widely in their technical methods and aims, since at the beginning membership in the Association did not rest upon any prerequisite training. In the early 30's, this organization was converted into a federation of local American societies. In 1937 a group of

* The American Psychoanalytic Association is not to be confused with the Section on Psychoanalysis of the American Psychiatric Association. Membership in the Section is evidence of an interest in the subject, but not of training in its use.

training institutes was recognized by the national body, and by mutual agreement minimal standards were established which now govern their activities and those of any new training groups which apply for recognition. This agreement is revised periodically to keep up with changing and developing experience.

By 1947 the local societies which made up the federation and the local training institutes which had been recognized by the national body had multiplied in numbers and grown in strength to a point where many of the functions of the central body could be handed over to the local societies and institutes. Thus in the development of the American Psychoanalytic Association as in the development of the International, there has been a healthy distribution of authority to the local groups. The American Psychoanalytic Association has thus become a direct membership society, a forum for scientific discussions, a guardian of standards, and an adviser on educational issues, but retaining little or no executive authority.

The Training Institutes and Centers

Not all of the societies which are affiliated with the American Psychoanalytic Association are large enough to organize their own training institutes. Each group as it grows, however, gradually assumes the responsibility for training psychiatrists in psychoanalysis. Originally all training institutes developed as part of psychoanalytic societies. Recently some institutes have formed independent of any society, some of them as special sub-divisions of the department of psychiatry of a medical school.

Because much of the instruction is on an individual basis, the ratio of teachers to students in psychoanalytic institutes must be high. A typical example is the New York Psychoanalytic Institute where there are about 60 instructors for a student body of 150 students. Another peculiar feature of psychoanalytic education is the one-to-one relationship of teacher to student both in the preparatory analysis and again in supervision. This creates a bottleneck at the initial and final stages of training.

Furthermore, it is important for each student to have contact with many analysts, so that his preparatory analysis, his seminars, his theoretical lectures, his technical lectures, and his supervised clinical work should not all be given by one small group of teachers. Any lack of balance in the presentation of theory and technique which may arise out of personal biases, can be turned to advantage if the influence of any individual teacher is balanced by contacts with many other viewpoints. All of this means that training units in psychoanalysis are most effective if they are large. Yet even those medical schools which are most hospitable to psychiatry in general, and which are beginning to be hospitable to psychoanalysis, can appoint only small numbers of psychiatrists and psychoanalysts to their staffs. Therefore it is likely that, whether this is desirable or not, for a considerable time to come, most psychoanalytic training will be given in institutes which are independent of universities.

The independent institute has certain other advantages. In the first place it is able to provide postgraduate training for members of the departments of psychiatry of all medical schools in its general neighborhood. As an example, a recent statistical survey indicated that a few years ago 90 per cent of the men teaching on the faculties of psychiatry of the medical schools in and around greater New York either were at that time or had been students at the New York Psychoanalytic Institute. Furthermore, at one time the same Institute was providing instruction to members of the faculties of medical schools in New Haven, Montreal, Toronto, Boston, Philadelphia, California, Denmark, Norway, Holland, and various South American countries, and to our own armed forces as well. Thus the concentration of available teaching personnel in the well-organized curriculum of a single institute can be an economy for all of the medical schools served by that institute, making it possible at the same time to give the students a broader and more varied interpretation of analysis than could be provided by a small psychoanalytic unit in any one medical school. Thus, size automatically saves an institute from becoming the unbalanced expression of any one viewpoint, or a factional representative either of so-called "orthodoxy" or of so-called "heterodoxy".

On the other hand, the independent institute also has certain disadvantages. (a) Because of their many and various outside responsibilities and allegiances, the students at such an institute are not as easy to control and supervise as they would be if all of their activities were concentrated in one organization which had the authority and prestige of medical schools. (b) Similarly it is more difficult for the unattached institute to select patients and to match them to the students according to their development and training. For this, clinical facilities are essential; and the unattached institute finds it difficult to assemble, sort, and distribute such clinical material. (c) For certain types of research work, hospital facilities with at least a few beds are essential. (d) It is difficult to finance independent institutes. All such institutes have discovered that Foundations and even many individuals do not recognize that these institutes are equivalent to a university department in a postgraduate medical school; consequently Foundations or individuals often refuse grants to Psychoanalytic Institutes, even while they provide funds for the medical schools whose psychiatrists these same institutes are training. This makes it difficult for institutes to create part-time fellowships and part-time jobs for students, to accumulate funds with which to place their faculties on part-time salaries, or to finance clinical facilities and research.

These considerations lead to the conclusion that a formal liaison should be worked out between existing independent institutes and medical schools, so as to integrate training in psychoanalysis with various phases of medical and psychiatric education.

The Organization of Training

In all Institutes and training centers, responsibility is placed in the hands of an educational committee which selects students from among the physicians who apply, organizes courses, appoints the faculty, supervises training and recommends students for graduation.

In many ways the selection of students is the most difficult task of all. It is easy to ascertain the general intellectual caliber and the academic record of the applicant and whether he can fulfil the formal training requirements. These include graduation from a Grade A medical school, a general medical internship, a thorough grounding in hospital psychiatry, and an adequate training in the fundamentals of neurology.

What is more difficult to ascertain is his aptitude for psychological work (Chapter XXIV) or the presence of subtly masked neurotic difficulties, which may affect both the quality of his work as an analyst and his vulnerability to the emotional stresses of the analyst's life. Therefore, each applicant is carefully scrutinized with this in mind by a special subcommittee of the educational committee. Different institutes are experimenting with many different procedures.*

The cost of psychoanalytic education is high both for the student and for the Institute, and its duration long. Therefore from a practical viewpoint alone it is of the utmost importance to the applicant and to the Institute to rule out as many unsuitable applicants as possible. From a scientific and social point of view, the value of eliminating those who might exploit analysis or become ill themselves is of obvious importance. This is why so much stress is laid on the process of selection.

(a) The Curriculum

Psychoanalytic education can be subdivided into five components: (1) the development of psychoanalytic insight into

* A panel dicussion of this whole problem will be found in the *Bulletin of the American Psychoanalytic Association*, Vol. 4, No. 3, September, 1948, pp. 29–36.

oneself, through the personal analysis; (2) training in the history of psychoanalytic concepts and theories; (3) education in the principles of psychoanalytic technique; (4) the theoretical application of psychoanalytic principles and techniques by participation in clinical seminars; and (5) finally, the practical experience of conducting the psychoanalytic treatment of selected patients under supervision.

Before beginning his preparatory analysis each student is required to pledge himself not to start psychoanalytic practice until this step is approved by the Educational Committee.

Thereafter, his first step in training is to become a patient in a training analysis, variously called the "didactic" or "preparatory" analysis. This analysis is conducted by a psychoanalyst who is on the faculty of the Institute. The duration of the training analysis varies considerably, the factors which determine its length being for the most part technical. Training analyses never last less than a year, however, and usually longer. It is generally believed that a training analysis must be at least as thorough and as deep as the therapeutic analyses which the candidate will ultimately conduct. Actually, the aim of every preparatory analysis is also therapeutic. This therapeutic goal is often elusive, since in the training analysis one is aiming at the illumination of subtly disguised and well-compensated personality weaknesses, trying not only to achieve intellectual clarity but also to strengthen the future analyst to withstand the severe emotional stresses to which he will be subjected throughout his future professional life.

After a certain point has been reached in the course of the preparatory analysis the student is allowed to attend theoretical and technical lectures, practical case discussions, reading courses and the like. This is his first formal contact with the teaching activities of the Institute; and it includes an opportunity to participate in the discussion of the progress of patients who are under analytic treatment by experienced instructors and advanced students. In such discussions the identity of the patient is never revealed.

As the student builds up his knowledge of theory and technique, selected patients are assigned to him for analysis. This analysis is conducted under the supervision of an experienced training analyst who is a member of the faculty. The student brings the supervisor the material of his work with the patient, usually at least once a week, for review, criticism, and suggestions. Here again, however, the identity of the patient is never disclosed.

After the successful conclusion of several such supervised analyses, the student's status is again reviewed by the Educational Committee, with reference to his pre-analytic experience and training, any additional formal training in psychiatry that may have been required during the intervening years since his original application, the quality of his work in seminars and case discussions, and his work both as a patient during his own preparatory analysis and as a psychoanalyst during the conduct of his supervised analyses, his grasp of theory and technique as evidenced in his reports on the analyses which he has conducted under supervision, and finally his general grasp as evidenced during a searching oral examination by a faculty committee.

The Training Institute as a Guild and as a Moral Influence

Most such Institutes are chartered in their respective states as recognized educational bodies. This gives them no legal power to enforce their exacting standards, but their moral influence is making itself felt increasingly. For many years training institutes have been conducted by psychoanalysts at the cost of much time, for which the faculty has not been remunerated. The faculty in most Institutes receives no salary. Running expenses have been met by dues paid by the analysts themselves and in a small part by tuition fees.

Recently, limited outside funds have become available to assist the work of a few of the Institutes.

The institutes exist not to limit the number of "competitors", but to train more young colleagues to become competent practitioners of psychoanalysis. The ultimate influence of the societies and of the institutes depends upon the support given them by physicians in general and by the public, a support which will be most effective if it takes the form of making sure that any man who claims to be a psychoanalyst is associated with one of the psychoanalytic societies and institutes recognized by the American Psychoanalytic Association.* Psychoanalytic Institutes have the further purpose of providing advanced training for members, for whose benefit advanced courses and advanced technical seminars are given in which new developments and research problems are discussed.

The Economics of Psychoanalytic Training

Four basic factors determine the economics of psychoanalytic education, and indirectly of psychoanalytic practice (cf. Chapter XVI). One is its duration. The second one is the fact that the prerequisites for psychoanalytic training take so many years to acquire that by the time a student is ready to start his analytic training he is usually in his thirties, married, and with a family to support. The third is that there are at present almost no endowments out of which to pay salaries to the faculty or fellowships to the students. The fourth is that there are few part-time jobs for the students which would enable them to earn a living and still keep part of each day free for study.

As a consequence, with few exceptions, psychoanalytic training is carried on at night. The instructors spend their days in the practice of psychoanalysis. The students spend theirs in general psychiatric practice, either privately or in psychiatric hospitals or out-patient clinics. Obviously, it is

* See Appendix.

impossible for work of the highest calibre to be done under these circumstances. Funds are needed to provide salaries for instructors, and fellowships and part-time jobs for students, to make training possible during the day. Everyone recognizes the urgency of this need, since the shortage of trained personnel is the bottleneck in any plan to make psychoanalytic therapy available to more people. Nevertheless many Institutes have found that it is extremely difficult to raise money for this essential purpose. For the present, therefore, our institutes for postgraduate medical training in psychoanalysis are forced to operate as medical night schools.

The duration of training is longer than is ordinarily realized. The minimal duration of the course is three years; it usually takes four to five. This depends in part on the duration of the preparatory analysis, and in part on difficulties which the student may encounter as he undertakes his supervised work, or in his advanced theoretical courses. This follows four years of medical school, an additional three to four years of internships and residencies in general medicine and in psychiatry, a variable period of work in outpatient clinics, child-guidance clinics, and if possible work with the psychiatric problems of medical and surgical wards. The beginning of psychoanalytic training can be introduced into this sequence after two years in a psychiatric hospital. Therefore, if the young physician knows from the start what he wants to do and begins his program immediately after graduation from medical school, the full further training will still take anywhere between eight and ten years. If, as often happens, the young physician experiments for two or three years before he makes his final choice of a career, the full period of training will take that much longer. As a result, before the war the average age of 100 consecutive physician-students on admission to the New York Psychoanalytic Institute was thirty-six years, their average age on graduation close to forty.

This creates a serious problem for society as a whole. It

means that the trained analyst has relatively few years in which to practice the technique which it has taken him so many years to master. This automatically limits the supply of trained analysts. As has been said earlier, it also creates a serious economic problem for the analyst himself, because he has few years in which to earn security for his old age and an education for his children. This is one reason for the relatively high cost of psychoanalysis. From the point of view of the community, it is one more reason why subsidies are needed to facilitate the training of more analysts, and why it is important to find some way in which the training can begin earlier without sacrificing either maturity or ability.

During the training period, the heaviest expenses for the student are his long years of low earning capacity and the cost of his preparatory analysis. Because the faculties of most institutes give their services without remuneration, the charges which the Institutes make to their students are relatively low when compared to those of other academic organizations.

This program constitutes a heavy drain on the time, energy, and financial resources of the faculty. The individual instructor conducts most preparatory analyses at reduced fees. As he becomes older and more experienced, more students seek to be trained by him; but with advancing age the instructor cannot work the long hours which this imposes on him, since he usually must take the student into training in addition to his schedule of patients and not in place of a patient. As the demand for psychoanalytic training grows, it will become necessary to find some means whereby the training analyst can be adequately compensated, if the whole system is not to break down.

The one important criticism which may justly be leveled against the existing system of training students is that it is not free from the dangers of rigidity and traditionalism. One cannot brush aside this criticism. Nevertheless, in this particular field of work, where the danger of untrained practice is great, the individual patient runs a lesser risk by turning to the carefully trained man, even if this long and difficult training costs the analyst some of his freedom and spontaneity, and science loses some of its momentum of change. In the long run, well-educated men do not remain slaves to any theoretical system. The existence of a normal amount of free growth and development within the psychoanalytic point of view is shown by the frequency with which it has been accused of inconsistencies that have arisen out of changes in theory and technique over the course of the years.

Training in non-Freudian Psychoanalysis

None of the earlier divergent schools of analytic thought, i.e., those of Adler, Jung, Rank, Stekel, etc., developed an organized plan of training. Some more recent groups have copied the general outlines of the plan described above.

This is not the place for a discussion of the differences between the theories of the Jungians, the Adlerians, the Burrows group, Stekel, the Rankians, Horney, Klein, etc. No one group can lay claim to a monopoly on truth. Certainly the Psychoanalytic Societies and Institutes which are recognized by the American or International bodies with their Freudian approach, can set up no claims to omniscience. They can justly claim, however, that their training regulations are fair and thorough, that any honest, healthy, nonneurotic, well-prepared, and intelligent physician can go through this apprenticeship, and that subsequently, on the basis of this fundamental discipline, he can develop his own ideas and test his own theories freely.

Furthermore, in this peculiarly confidential field of medical practice it is only by working in such institutes as these that a physician can be given an opportunity to subject his work to the scrutiny and criticism of his colleagues. More than any other branch of medicine, psychotherapy has to be conducted in privacy. This makes it peculiarly difficult to know just how a colleague works. The only way to increase one's own skill by study of the techniques of others is through the apprenticeship of the Institute. This is a further reason why it is sound to insist that experiments with modifications in technique must rest upon a mastery of existing techniques.

Finally it should be borne in mind that from the viewpoint of patients the only important part of the struggle over so-called Freudian "orthodoxy" is concerned not with matters of theory, but with the problems of technique. No one accuses a surgeon of being too orthodox because he subjects himself to the rigid discipline of aseptic surgery. No one accuses an experimenter of being too orthodox if he scrupulously avoids introducing unknown variables into a complex experimental situation. Similarly, everything that is rigid and formal in psychoanalytic method has grown out of the necessity to carry on psychotherapy in a situation in which external variables are reduced to a minimum, since it is only in this way that the production of psychological data can be free, unguided, and undistorted. Without a technique to maintain constancy in the therapeutic situation, there can be no such thing as psychoanalysis. Important though the inner gift may be for the student of psychology, it is no adequate substitute for discipline and training in the use of a highly complex instrument.

In certain instances, either the theories or the practices of the various divergent groups, or both, are diametrically opposed to some aspect of the Freudian approach. In other instances a single concept is given undue emphasis and is regarded as an adequate substitute for that which is omitted or rejected. It is significant that the early dissenting group gave up the use of the word "psychoanalysis" in order to disassociate themselves from Freud, and referred to their position as "anti-Freudian"; whereas all of the more recent deviants insist that they are analysts and that they are not *anti-*, but only *neo-*Freudian. This ferment is healthy, as long as it does not lead to any reduction in the standards of a fundamental and inclusive basic training. Our position is that the fundamental training should be the same for all, and that experiments leading to the modifications of theory and technique should be conducted by men who have been thoroughly schooled and experienced in existing theory and technique. New "schools" of theory and technique should not be proclaimed as great new revelations; nor should they be broadcast to the laity in popular books or taught in "unorthodox" institutes before they have been carefully and thoroughly tested before a jury of fellow-scientists. This is the way medical science progresses.

Chapter XXIII

THE PROBLEM OF THE NON-MEDICAL PSYCHOANALYST

Few psychoanalytic controversies have been more heated or more confused than those which have centered around the question of whether it is wise to train non-medical men to give psychoanalytic treatments, and especially whether laymen so trained should be allowed to treat people who are psychologically ill. No one questions the advisability of allowing non-medical scientists to use psychoanalysis for investigative purposes.

The issue arose originally because of events which occurred during the early days of psychoanalysis. In Vienna, for many years the opposition to psychoanalysis on the part of the medical profession was intransigent. The medical schools fostered this attitude in young physicians, so that their minds were closed to the newly developing system of psychological theories and techniques. In time this embittered Freud himself, and his early followers naturally banded together for mutual encouragement and moral support against the hostile medical world. These early students of psychoanalysis came from many disciplines and many backgrounds. Among them were artists, writers, psychologists, educators, parents, religious leaders, lawyers, journalists, anthropologists and a scattering of psychiatrists. Since at that time there was no academic recognition of the value of studying Freud's work, most of those who came to him came either out of a need for personal therapy, or as in the case of the few psychiatrists and other scientists, because their interest had been kindled in the new psychological world which psychoanalytic literature described. Thus, many of the laymen were "lay" not merely in their lack of a medical training, but also in the absence of any general scientific background, and especially in their lack of a fundamental training in scientific methodology. Nevertheless many showed considerable psychological aptitude, and of these some decided to professionalize their interest in psychoanalysis by undertaking to practice psychoanalysis in the treatment of others. Consequently, among these early analysts, non-medical men played an important role. In certain instances, however, the lack of a general scientific training permitted uncontrolled speculations to pose as scientific hypotheses. The difference between such speculations and the responsible formulation of verifiable hypotheses was not always clear to them (cf. Rank, Klein, and others). It is hard to say whether, in balance, the positive contributions of these non-scientific analysts outweigh the confusion they have caused.

As psychoanalysis has come to occupy an increasingly important place in psychiatric education, the role of the non-medical scientist in psychoanalysis has become a controversial issue. There are those who feel that he should play no role at all in psychoanalytic therapy, and that his psychoanalytic activities should be restricted to its applications to anthropology, art, sociology, education, and research. The arguments of these opponents of lay analysis must not be brushed aside lightly. They point to the fact that American medicine has had a more open-minded and hospitable attitude towards psychoanalysis than was true in Europe; and they are afraid of jeopardizing the close integration of psychoanalytic psychiatry into American medicine in general. They feel that irrespective of the merits of the case, for the time being at any rate, it would be strategically unwise to allow laymen to play any role in therapy, lest this widen again the old breach between the psychological and the organic aspects of medical therapy, precisely at a time when a harmonious interrelation between them is being established.

Furthermore, these critics point to certain deficiencies which the layman not infrequently brings to therapeutic procedures. There is the danger that in his eager search for psychological causes which can be reached by psychological methods, and because he does not understand the nature of organic illness, the lay analyst may overlook early warning symptoms of physical disease. Some lay analysts become defensive towards organic medicine, which may lead them to neglect adequate checks. Others over-compensate by sending patients for superfluous physical check-ups, thus playing into a patient's hypochondriacal tendencies. The critics of lay analysis are afraid also of the layman's naive enthusiasm for therapy, an enthusiasm which centuries of lessons learned painfully at the autopsy table have taught physicians to curb with rigid skepticism and self-criticism. They are afraid of the layman's lack of a fully developed sense of therapeutic responsibility and of his lack of that basic scientific training which is needed if the therapist is to use sound critique in evaluating his results. The further argument is advanced that especially in psychotherapy the interplay of physical and psychological factors must be watched carefully at all times. Physical disturbances can be superimposed on psychological illness and vice versa, and sometimes it is far from easy to demarcate the boundary between the two. It is fair to assume that in such cases the medically trained psychoanalyst will approach such problems with less danger either of underestimating the hints of organic illness or of exaggerating them.

On the other hand, the supporters of the analytically trained lay therapist believe, with this writer, that an adequate curriculum could and should be established by law, which would provide fundamental training in the basic sciences and in the self-critical methods of scientific work, specific training in physiology and psychology, both normal and abnormal, and finally in all psychotherapeutic techniques and especially in psychoanalysis. Such a man could be given a Doctorate in Medical Psychology, and licensed specifically to practice psychotherapy and psychoanalysis. His patients could be protected by two further safeguards: (a) he could be licensed to accept patients for treatment only after a thorough medical and psychiatric examination; and (b) he could be enjoined by law to send all patients for medical reexamination periodically throughout the course of the treatment. Theoretically, therefore, if the lay analyst had adequate training and if his right to practice were safeguarded by adequate legally specified restrictions, it should be possible to protect any patient who is being analyzed by a trained layman against the dangers either of overlooking organic disease or of making mountains out of organic molehills.

Possible Gains vs. Immediate Dangers

It may well be asked, however, whether there are any advantages to be derived from the therapeutic practice of psychoanalysis by people who are not trained in medicine. This question is difficult to answer in general terms. From the point of view of psychoanalysis as a science, much can be contributed by men who are trained in such fields as anthropology, ethnology, philology, mythology, education, psychology, sociology, the law, and the like. Psychoanalysis needs their special knowledge and experience. Nor is it humanly possible for any one physician to master these allied fields in addition to the medical disciplines and psychoanalysis. If representatives of these allied disciplines are to make as full a contribution as possible, they must have a thorough training in psychoanalysis; and if this training is to be inclusive, it should include at least some measure of experience in its therapeutic application.

It is impossible, therefore, to make any general rule as to the best policy to pursue; and in different countries psychoanalytic institutes have different rules about training nonmedical students. For many years, however, American medicine has had to carry on a fight to rid the American scene

of untrained and unscrupulous charlatans and of many therapeutic cults. With this long struggle in mind, physicians
are reluctant to open the door to the practice of any form of
therapy by medically untrained people, however upright their
motives and however skillful their personal techniques. They
fear that a lowering of the barriers against non-medical
therapy in any direction might result in the end in a lowering of the barriers in other directions as well.

Hence, this is one of those not infrequent issues in which
long-term scientific advantages must be balanced against
immediate social considerations, since under certain circumstances even considerable scientific gains can be socially ill-
advised or ill-timed.

At present the official policy of the American Psychoanalytic Association, and of all institutes which it recognizes, is
opposed to the training of non-physicians in the therapeutic
applications of psychoanalysis.

To many people, however, it seems that if it is ever safe
to make an exception to the general rule against non-medical
therapists, it is in the field of psychoanalytic psychotherapy.
Where no struggle against charlatans has had to be waged, or
where it has been successfully won many years before,
a community may safely adopt a broader policy towards the
training of laymen for the therapeutic practice of psychoanalysis; always provided, of course, that the lay practitioner
will subject himself to training requirements as rigid and
exacting as those to which psychoanalytic institutes now subject the physician who comes to them for training.

One cannot, however, evaluate this problem solely in terms
of theoretical scientific values. There are in addition some
important practical and cultural implications of the participation of laymen in psychotherapy, and certain implications for
medical education in general. Here we are confronted with
certain basic facts. First among these is the fact that the
ordinary physician is as untrained in psychotherapy as is the

ordinary layman. Through failure to understand fundamental principles of psychotherapy he is capable of doing as much harm as the lay analyst may do through ignorance of the fundamental principles of bodily disease. Secondly, we must face the fact that for many years clergymen who are interested in pastoral counselling, clinical psychologists, educators, and social workers have all been practicing psychotherapy, and not infrequently analytical psychotherapy or even full-fledged psychoanalysis. Thirdly, anyone who considers objectively the overall picture of medical education in this country will realize that our existing facilities will never be able to train enough physicians, either in general psychotherapy or in psychoanalysis, to meet community needs. These needs include psychiatric service in schools from kindergarten through college, in courts, in social agencies, in industry, in general hospitals, and a more adequate staffing of out-patient psychiatric clinics and psychiatric hospitals, not to mention the needs of private psychiatric practice. In the American Psychiatric Association in May, 1949, there were 5,300 psychiatrists, of whom 4,000 work full-time in psychiatric hospitals, leaving about 1,300 for all community services and for private practice. It has been conservatively estimated that we need between 6,000 and 10,000 psychiatrists for duty in psychiatric hospitals, and about 20,000 for community services and private practice. Medical education is adding to this number at a rate of perhaps 150 psychiatrists a year, which is barely enough to take care of the annual loss of personnel through old age, illness and death.

These statistics alone have convinced some medical educators that we must evolve, under the auspices of our medical schools and teaching hospitals a new therapeutic discipline, i.e., a doctorate in medical psychology. They feel that laymen should be trained specifically for psychotherapy in medical schools and in teaching hospitals, where they will have an opportunity to acquire broad clinical experience and certain important habits of the medical mind, namely, the dedication to therapeutic responsibility, the respect for the patient's right to privacy and anonymity, a familiarity with the phenomena of organic disease, the objective skepticism which the well-trained physician feels for all over-enthusiastic therapeutic claims, etc. The advocates of such a doctorate in medical psychology also argue that certain parts of the medical curriculum could be eliminated from the curriculum of the new discipline, with the result that, instead of taking twelve to fifteen years after college (the time needed to complete the training of a psychiatrist in psychotherapeutic techniques), the doctor in medical psychology could be thoroughly trained in six to eight years after college.

This plan would have many advantages: (a) a non-medical psychotherapist who was trained in this way would not be a layman, but a well-trained and well-rounded scientist in clinical and therapeutic psychology; (b) he would have acquired a medical viewpoint and habit of mind through being trained in a medical atmosphere; (c) he would understand the essentials of normal and pathological human physiology; (d) he would have had the invaluable experience of working psychologically with patients who suffer from organic as well as psychological illnesses; (e) he would be trained in all psychological techniques far more fully than is the average young psychiatrist; (f) finally, instead of finishing his training between the ages of 35 and 40, he would finish it somewhere between the ages of 28 and 33, with the consequence that each such practitioner would have that many more years before him in which to use his skills in the service of the community. Under such a plan, the same educational facilities could train twice as many therapists in the same length of time; and treatment services would, consequently, become available in the community in greater abundance and at lower cost. Finally, with adequate legal safeguards there need be no loss of security from the point of view of the organic welfare of the patient.

The problem is complicated and there are many things to be said on both sides of it.   It is the subject of investigation and discussion today by many thoughtful medical educators, and by many Foundations interested in the improvement of medical education.*

* The readers especially interested in this topic are referred to the following detailed discussions of the issues:

Freud, S.: *The Problem of Lay-Analysis*, Brentano's, New York, 1927, 186 pp.

Symposium on Lay Analysis in *International Journal of Psycho-Analysis*, Vol. 8, 1927, pp. 174–283.

Kubie, L. S.: Medical Responsibility for Training in Clinical Psychology, *Journal, Association of American Medical Colleges*, March, 1948, Vol. 8, pp. 1–8.

The Josiah Macy, Jr. Foundation: *Transactions of Conference on Training in Clinical Psychology*, March 27–28, 1947, New York City.

Chapter XXIV

THE APTITUDE FOR PSYCHOLOGICAL WORK

Psychoanalysis focuses its attention on the investigation and relief of many forms of human suffering and discontent. From these studies it has learned that most psychic pain is the product of subtly disguised neurotic processes which are at work in the lives of every "normal" human being. This finding has forced us to face the sorry fact that we do not yet know how to bring up our children free from transient neurotic episodes which leave scars for which in adult years we pay a high price. It is not strange, therefore, that among those who become interested in psychiatry and psychoanalysis, many are drawn to it by their own struggles with unhappiness. The influence of personal unhappiness and maladjustment on the effectiveness of the future analyst depends on several factors, some of which are grouped together under the general heading of "psychological aptitudes."

Psychological aptitude is one of those human attributes which is more easily recognized than measured or defined or analyzed into its components. Indeed, institutes for the training of psychoanalysts are currently making extensive investigations into its nature, because an evaluation of potential psychological aptitude is of major importance in the screening of applicants. Presumably this gift must have its roots in a subjective experience of emotional stress and strain which has been frankly faced, and out of which develops the capacity to identify with the pains and joys of others. This is what enables one man to sense what others are going through and to relate it in some degree to his own experiences. Finally psychological aptitude probably requires some degree of confidence in one's ability to recognize and appraise intuitively the expressions, gestures, and intonations of others and the sequences of mood and content in their speech. Something of all this must go into that elusive and subtle talent which we call "psychological aptitude"; but its exact make-up and its precise sources have never been ascertained. Not even its relationship to suffering is entirely clear.

There is a widespread belief that all sufferers from neuroses are "introverts" and that all "extraverts" are neurosis-free. This is entirely false. Although certain types of neuroses force their victims to attend closely to their own feelings, other neuroses serve as an effective defense against any self-awareness. Consequently among those who suffer from frank neuroses, one patient will constantly feel his own emotional pulse, while the next never stops to ask whether he has any emotions. Therefore, it would not be true to say either that all sufferers from neuroses are over-emotional, or that all individuals who are preoccupied with their own emotional difficulties are necessarily more neurotic than those who seem to have none, or that either group has problems which are more difficult or less readily soluble than those of the other. These are merely two quite automatic ways of handling neurotic problems. Naturally, however, the self-aware individual is likely to have more psychological aptitude than the other.

Another factor seems to be related to the age at which the individual first becomes aware. No human beings go through life without periods of turmoil. There are some whose neurotic mechanisms manifest themselves early but who compensate and subside quickly; others, whose neuroses appear early and never subside; and there is still a third group who to the casual observer seem more stable at the start of life, but whose hidden problems become manifest as neurotic symptoms only in the thirties or forties. Many "campus heroes" come to neurotic grief in these years; and it is a fallacy to think of the pseudo-normality of their early years as a standard of healthy adjustment. Again such differences in timing are not differences in kind; but their effects on life and consequently on the consciousness of suffering vary widely. One may say that, in general, those who put on a bold front through early maturity tend all through life to hide from their own emotions and from those of others, and therefore have a limited ability to understand and sympathize with psychological problems. It is primarily this which accounts for the supercilious contempt with which people who have been able to hide from their own pain look down on those who acknowledge suffering more humbly and frankly. They could not face with tolerance and sympathy the pain of others, without being forced to face and accept their own.

Therefore for the sake of man's understanding of his own nature, it is fortunate that there are always some men who early in life are forced to ponder on their own capacity for happiness and unhappiness, men who, with Thoreau, wonder why it is that "all men lead lives of quiet desperation." These individuals tend to become what is called "psychologically minded"; and it is quite inevitable that those who make it their profession to study the problem of human discontent should come largely from this group.

Many factors determine when in life an individual will first be forced to face his emotional problems. For all individuals alike the struggle begins in infancy over the feelings of helplessness and inadequacy at the frustration of unattainable yearnings, a frustration which in time generates impotent rage and fear. This starts long before there is any conscious awareness of variations in the outer circumstances of life. In the later management of that struggle, however, the feelings which are emphasized and confirmed by the circumstances of life acquire increasing power and significance. Advantageous and reassuring circumstances, such as wealth, membership in a dominant group, unusual athletic prowess, great beauty, special talents, etc., tend frequently, though not always, to obscure the subtler inner conflicts. Conversely, disadvantageous circumstances during the developmental years accentuate the inner doubts, and focus the sufferer's attention on them. Especially is this true when the external situation seems to single out a child for scorn for reasons which are beyond his control, as for instance because of his national or religious origins or the color of his skin. Indeed, for every man his origins can be a particularly important source either of reassurance or of self-depreciation. To come from "important people", to belong to a "great" nation, to have an illustrious ancestor, becomes in most instances a prop to a child; whereas to come from a group which is scorned feeds the fires of self-doubt which smoulder in everyone.

That is why members of all alien minorities find that even where they are subjected only to petty social discriminations, these exaggerate the feelings of insecurity in the youth of that group. Such petty hurts affect young schoolchildren before they have learned adequate methods of dealing with discrimination and masking its pain. Consequently, children from minority groups soon tend to become either over-aggressive, or over-sensitive, and live with a frank awareness of insecurity and self-doubt. Inevitably these circumstances increase their emotional vulnerability. When this is directed into productive channels, it can serve as a spur to intellectual, artistic, and economic productivity. This accounts in part for the disproportionate role which artists of continental origin have played in all Anglo-Saxon cultures. At the same time it also accounts for the extraordinary interest in psychiatry and psychoanalysis on the part of members of minority groups.

The practice of psychoanalysis demands both a high degree of technical training and a large measure of psychological aptitude. The latter can be found in every sphere of life, and in every racial, religious and social milieu. In no country is the practice of psychoanalysis an exclusively or even predominantly Jewish activity, although in a few large centers of population the percentage of Jews among analysts is high. Under existing conditions this is inevitable and natural because as long as the position of the Jew in the world retains its present anomalies, one must expect to find a large number of Jews consciously attentive to their own inner struggles, and turning from these to a concern for the psychological needs of others. Just so long therefore, will the Jew continue to be an active participant in the development of psychiatry in general and of psychoanalysis in particular.

Although the circumstances affect all minority groups, they exercise a special influence on the Jew. This fact, and the fact that Freud himself was a Jew, has led some critics to ask whether or not psychoanalysis should be looked upon as a "Jewish science", i.e., a system of ideas which bears the stamp of a particular theological system or of a particular emotional attitude to life and its problems. The question itself could scarcely be asked seriously about any other scientific theory. The theory of relativity is not "Jewish", just because Einstein is a Jew. If a Christian mathematician uses the theory in computing the answer to some problem, his answer is not therefore a Jewish answer. Obviously, psychoanalysis is not "Jewish" merely because Freud was a Jew. Furthermore, psychoanalysis uses as its chief implement the method of free association, which was derived from the earlier work of a German Protestant, which was subsequently investigated in many other connections by psychologists of many lands and many faiths.

Of even greater moment, however, is the fact that the essence of psychoanalysis is not a body of doctrines, but a technique which is applied by many and varied human beings to the study and treatment of the problems of other human beings. Catholic psychoanalysts treat Jewish or Protestant patients, and vice versa. The majority of analysts and of analytical patients do not come from any one religious faith, nor from any one national or racial group.

As we have already indicated, the relation of psychological aptitude to neuroses, healed and unhealed, is an important practical problem for every training institute (cf. Chapter

XXII), and cannot be fully dealt with here. The fact that early in his life the analyst may have had to deal with some type of neurotic disturbance in his own personality can be a positive asset to him in his later work. Indeed, even analysts who have been quite sick psychologically, and in whom a not inconsiderable amount of illness persists, may possess great theoretical brilliance. This does not mean, however, that the analyst must remain sick in order to retain his psychological aptitudes. Such sensitivity is never lost in the healing process; and in the training of the analyst a major emphasis is laid on the therapeutic effect of the training analysis, without fear that the student will thereby lose his ability to estimate the moods and feelings of others.

There is no general agreement on the forms of neurosis which may leave advantageous residues in the make-up of the analyst, or what forms should constitute grounds for turning down the application of a would-be student. This is a matter which is being subjected to investigation. The fact must be faced, however, that in the training of the young analyst the process of therapy can at times present special difficulties, and that in spite of the therapeutic purpose of the training analysis its therapeutic leverage is not as great as that of the analytic process when it deals with patients. Perhaps it is fair to say that in training we often start with an individual who is more than usually vulnerable to emotional stress, and try to make him less vulnerable than the average, so as to enable him to withstand a life which is full of exceptionally severe emotional strains. It is not surprising that the training process does not always attain this goal, or that in their personalities and in their lives even mature and able analysts may show the fact that they are not free from internal conflicts and stresses. From the point of view of the patient, however, it is essential only that these residues of earlier neurotic difficulties shall not under any circumstances interfere with the analyst's objective attitude towards his patient's problems or with his therapeutic relationship to the patient himself.

V. Retrospect and Prospect

Chapter XXV

CONTROVERSIES AND FRONTIERS

The Techniques of Scientific Controversy

In Chapter XVII we quoted Claude Bernard's astute comment that scientists are like other human beings, insofar as all men suffer from the same vulnerability to bias. In addition to this internal source of error, scientists are not infrequently subjected to social pressures, which may further warp intellectual judgments. Such external pressures are particularly strong in any science which stirs popular prejudices, or whose conclusions influence health and welfare directly. There are always some scientists who find it difficult to resist such pressures, and who wittingly or unwittingly shape their scientific convictions to curry popular favor or to win the support of Foundations. As Claude Bernard implied, scientists are human beings; and analysts are no exception.

This flaw in human nature has played a significant role in the history of science. A gross example is the controversy over genetics which recently arose in Russia. Subtler manifestations of the influence of external pressure are seen in certain psychoanalytic controversies. Among these is the argument over the relative influence of cultural and biogenetic factors in the development of the neuroses. Another is the disagreement among psychoanalysts over the value of briefer forms of psychotherapy or of attempts to treat large groups of people simultaneously. These pressures which arise from social needs can have both good and bad effects. They prevent complacency, but they may also lead men to make incautious claims. The mere fact that work is done under pressure does not, of itself, invalidate the work (witness the developments of radar and of atomic energy during the War), but it adds immensely to the necessity for caution.

To be self-critical about research in therapy is harder than in any other field, because therapeutic research generates so much wishful thinking both in the investigator and in the public that is waiting impatiently for help. When to this source of error is added a vigorous popular demand for quick and easy cures, the dangers of quick and easy research and of exaggerated claims are multiplied many times. None of these considerations lessens the importance of the attempt to find brief and economical forms of analytical therapy. They merely place on all who may undertake to do research in this difficult field the responsibility not to make popular claims until their findings have been checked repeatedly by their scientific peers and colleagues. Specifically, this means that new departures in theory and technique should not be announced to the public in popular books and magazines before these "new" ways have been presented in technical journals, where their validity can be tested by other scientists.

So important is this principle, that it is fair to say that the human value of scientific controversy depends on the scrupulousness with which conflicting claims are tested *before* they are presented to the laity. This is an essential social responsibility in the relationship of science to society.

It is well to bear in mind the fact that like all human activities research is born of emotions which have some of their roots in frustration. Sometimes this frustration arises from the work itself, sometimes from unrelated aspects of the scientist's life. Thus the research impulse may be driven by domestic unhappiness, or by personal rivalry and ambition, or by a need to be important, or by other human foibles, as well as by larger and more generous human aspirations. If each notion is immediately proclaimed as a great new discovery which will solve all problems and cure all ills, the unconscious emotional forces that infused the research are likely to warp the intellectual processes, with the result that the research itself and the subsequent scientific controversy will become a source of popular confusion. If on the other hand the scientist's findings are subjected to clinical or experimental tests before they are broadcast to the public, then the conscious and unconscious sources of the investigator's activities remain a matter of private concern to the investigator alone, and not a matter of public concern. Therefore society should leave science alone, in the sense that it must not warp the truth either with prejudice or with undue urgency; and in return science must leave society undisturbed by its internal controversies, putting forth no unproven claims to a waiting and needy world. The more urgent the human need, the more silent should be the scientist. Atomic energy was not released by a war of words in the popular press.

Violations of this elementary principle have marred in some measure the history of psychoanalysis. Here, controversy as such has not been any more frequent or more heated than in other scientific fields. Equally violent feuds have arisen in physics and chemistry, or about such a seemingly innocent question as whether certain blood cells arise from one type of parent cell or from two. Whenever such controversies influence directly the treatment of sick people, the public follows them with an intense interest. Consequently, in matters of health, a public parade of controversy does more harm than it would over issues which are more abstract and remote. To dissent is healthy. It is not the fact of psychoanalytic controversy, but the manner and manners of it which have been deplorable; and it is a sin against man and against science to parade dissension publicly, and to proclaim oneself a new analytic messiah, thereby gathering proselytes who must of necessity come largely from the uncritical laity. We would do better to follow the example ᵗ by Freud himself, who worked for ten years in almost ˡ obscurity, before the impact of his work was felt by the Ɬc world at large. None among the rest of us have ʼourselves to a similar self-discipline.

ˑsies among psychoanalysts fall into two major

entist's findings are subjected to clinical or e[x]
tests before they are broadcast to the public,
scious and unconscious sources of the investiga
s remain a matter of private concern to the inv
lone, and not a matter of public concern. There
should leave science alone, in the sense that it must
e truth either with prejudice or with undue urge[n]
return science must leave society undisturbed by
controversies, putting forth no unproven claims t
and needy world. The more urgent the human ne
re silent should be the scientist. Atomic energy w
ased by a war of words in the popular press.
ations of this elementary principle have marred
measure the history of psychoanalysis. Here, co
y as such has not been any more frequent or mor
than in other scientific fields. Equally violent feud
isen in physics and chemistry, or about such a seem
nnocent question as whether certain blood cells aris[e]
e type of parent cell or from two. Whenever such
ersies influence directly the treatment of sick people,
lic follows them with an intense interest. Conse-
, in matters of health, a public parade of controversy
ore harm than it would over issues which are more
t and remote. To dissent is healthy. It is not the
psychoanalytic controversy, but the manner and man-
it which have been deplorable; and it is a sin against
d against science to parade dissension publicly, and
laim oneself a new analytic messiah, thereby gathering
tes who must of necessity come largely from the
cal laity. We would do better to follow the example
Freud himself, who worked for ten years in almost
scurity, before the impact of his work was felt by the
ic world at large. None among the rest of us have
ed ourselves to a similar self-discipline.
roversies among psychoanalysts fall into two major

XXII), and cannot be fully dealt with here. The fact that early in his life the analyst may have had to deal with some type of neurotic disturbance in his own personality can be a positive asset to him in his later work. Indeed, even analysts who have been quite sick psychologically, and in whom a not inconsiderable amount of illness persists, may possess great theoretical brilliance. This does not mean, however, that the analyst must remain sick in order to retain his psychological aptitudes. Such sensitivity is never lost in the healing process; and in the training of the analyst a major emphasis is laid on the therapeutic effect of the training analysis, without fear that the student will thereby lose his ability to estimate the moods and feelings of others.

There is no general agreement on the forms of neurosis which may leave advantageous residues in the make-up of the analyst, or what forms should constitute grounds for turning down the application of a would-be student. This is a matter which is being subjected to investigation. The fact must be faced, however, that in the training of the young analyst the process of therapy can at times present special difficulties, and that in spite of the therapeutic purpose of the training analysis its therapeutic leverage is not as great as that of the analytic process when it deals with patients. Perhaps it is fair to say that in training we often start with an individual who is more than usually vulnerable to emotional stress, and try to make him less vulnerable than the average, so as to enable him to withstand a life which is full of exceptionally severe emotional strains. It is not surprising that the training process does not always attain this goal, or that in their personalities and in their lives even mature and able analysts may show the fact that they are not free from internal conflicts and stresses. From the point of view of the patient, however, it is essential only that these residues of earlier neurotic difficulties shall not under any circumstances interfere with the analyst's objective attitude towards his patient's problems or with his therapeutic relationship to the patient himself.

areas: controversies over psychoanalytic theory and controversies over psychoanalytic technique. These are related of course; but frequently they have started independently, and they can most easily be described separately.

Controversies Over Theory

The early theoretical controversies were over the role of sex in the conflicts which produce neuroses. The dissenters moved in various directions. Breuer, Freud's first co-worker, could not accept Freud's evidence that unrecognized erotic impulses could invade even the relationship of the patient to the doctor, and must therefore be dealt with in therapy in such a way as to clarify the patient's understanding of this aspect of his life. Some years later Adler also turned his back on sexual conflict, substituting an almost exclusive emphasis on a blind drive for power and on the tendency to over-compensate for bodily weakness, whether real or fancied, with hostility and aggressiveness (Adler is responsible for that over-worked cliché, "inferiority complex"). In those early years, much of this was a valuable addition to psychoanalytic theory, and was promptly incorporated into analytic theory and practice. Unfortunately in his effort to prove that sexual conflicts were unimportant in the genesis of the neurosis, Adler went so far as to look upon the sexual drives themselves as largely a competitive struggle with the outside world. Furthermore, for reasons that are not entirely clear, Adler not only minimized the importance of guilt and fear over sexual conflicts, but also paid little attention to the difference between the effects of conflicts of which we are conscious and of conflicts of which we are unconscious. Little remains today of Adler's teachings, except those parts which have been incorporated into Freudian theory and technique.

As might have been expected, Adler's effort to prove that sex was of little importance was soon balanced by Stekel's attempt to prove that it was all-important, an effort which in a curious and distorted fashion is paralleled today by the fantastic speculations of Wilhelm Reich, to which no analyst of any school subscribes.

The next effort to dispose of sex as a source of significant neurotic difficulty was made by Carl G. Jung of Zurich. By stages, Jung came to substitute for the individual's struggles with his own developmental processes the notion that the source of the neurosis was to be found in a struggle with a quasi-mystical, universal or "collective" unconscious. Here again there was at the start some overlap between the Freudian and the Jungian concepts. Freud, too, was concerned with the possibility that unconscious thought and feeling might therefore be more or less universal, and relatively independent of individual experience. To Freud, however, these always remained a group of accessory forces whose existence and possible influence he was forced to consider seriously, since they might supplement and complicate the effects of experience. The existence of inherited patterns of unconscious conflict never became a cornerstone in Freud's concept of the unconscious, as it did for Jung; and never did inherited patterns seem to Freud to operate as a collective mystical force, apart from their manifestations, both conscious and unconscious, in each human being. Furthermore, Jung's almost mystical concept of a collective unconscious took a malignant turn during the war, when he used it as a pseudo-rational excuse for his outspoken flirtation with the Nazis and Nazi ideology.

Jungians in America are few and far between; and they are decreasing in number except in certain centers where they have become Freudian in all but name. Furthermore, American Jungians vary widely in the degree to which they accept Jung's formulation in all its implications, and consequently in the degree to which they follow him in his rejection of the simple earthy struggles over unconscious loves and hates on which Freudian theory and therapy are based.

After Jung there were for some years no further disagreements about the role of sex or of aggression in the genesis of the neurotic process. Recently, however, Horney and her adherents returned to a new version of this ancient issue, offering the pressure of modern cultural and environmental stresses as a timely alternative to the struggle with instinctual processes. She writes of the neurotic problems "of our times," overlooking the fact that there is no evidence that the neuroses of today differ in any but their superficial symptomatology from the neuroses of our ancestors. In Horney's confused theoretical structure there is the further implication that environmental stresses can operate apart from the instinctual forces in individual development. Thus Horney and her followers minimize the importance of what they call the "genetic" or instinctual struggles and of the unconscious residues of early troubles, attributing neurotic difficulties largely to current situational problems and to certain neurotic "trends" which the individual's past has engraved on his personality. This is, indeed, a perplexing paradox, since the neurotic distortion of the personality is itself the most important product of the neurotic process rather than its cause.

In terms of simple common sense these ideas would seem to be the strangest and least psychological of the various deviations. The superficial forms of the neuroses have varied from culture to culture and from age to age; but the neurotic process as such is not a product of modern times, and there is not one shred of statistical evidence to show that there has been any increase in the incidence of the neurotic process in modern man. The most that can be claimed is that the price man pays for his neurotic infirmities has changed, and that in certain respects it has increased. This makes a significant difference in the fate of the neurotic process, but has nothing to do with its genesis.

By implication, another theoretical controversy arises out of this "cultural" viewpoint, a controversy that has cropped up repeatedly and in changing forms during the short history of psychoanalysis. This is over the question of how early in the life of an individual one can find the roots of neurotic trouble. Freud first looked for the origins of the neurosis in some upsetting experiences, usually during puberty or early adolescence. Clinical experience soon proved, however, that many of these "events" were either wholly imaginary or else largely embellished with unconscious childish fantasies, and that consequently even where there had been a real traumatic experience, the event itself was only a small part of the total psychological experience. As Freud came to recognize the role of fantasy in these traumatic experiences, it also became clear to him that the earlier these happened the more important they were. Moreover, in the course of time, his emphasis shifted from single or even repeated traumatic events to those long-continued stressful situations which are an integral part of family life and of the process of growth (cf. Chapters II and III). With these shifting and evolving emphases, there have been recurring disagreements as to how early such situations exercise their destructive influences. Freud's major concern was always with the years between two or three and puberty. Various deviants have gone in the only two directions possible, some emphasizing earlier years, some later.

Otto Rank first went everybody else one better, and for a time attributed all of man's difficulties to the initial traumatic experience of being born. This was a notion which Freud never accepted, and which Rank himself subsequently abandoned. Unfortunately, there still have been no adequate studies of the long-run effects of different kinds of labor and delivery on subsequent psychological development. More recently Melanie Klein and her followers have taken a position which is almost as extreme as Rank's. They believe that they can recognize in the events of the first six months of life a psychological impact which can be either critically formative or destructive for an entire lifetime. At the other extreme is Horney, who minimizes the importance of early years, and emphasizes the current problem as Adler had done before her, and also Rank in a later phase of his development.

This preoccupation with the age at which trouble starts has taken several forms. Freud gradually came to emphasize a somewhat rigid series of phases in the development of the sexual and aggressive instincts. This point of view finally was called the *Instinct* or *Libido Theory*, and led to various attempts to derive personality traits and different constellations of neurotic symptoms from a constitutional over-activity of some particular phase of instinctual development, or from a fixation at that phase by a traumatic experience or by external stresses which happened to occur as the child was passing through that period of his life. This working hypothesis still governs the thinking of many analysts; but evidence as to the limits of its validity is far from complete. Furthermore, the theory itself has undergone many speculative and verbal vicissitudes, with little experimental testing. Fundamental research remains to be done in this area.

It is an interesting commentary on the role of the human personality in scientific progress that two analysts of approximately the same generation, who had trained under the same teachers, should turn to such diametrically opposed extremes as do Horney and Klein: one seeking the explanation of psychopathology in the experiences of the first months of life, and the other seeking explanations in the stressful present. In view of what we know of the identity of opposites in unconscious psychological processes, the genesis of such polarities is not hard to understand clinically; but they clutter up the pages of scientific history with needless and sterile controversies.

One can recognize in this disagreement an old scientific conflict in modern dress. The question whether the neurotic process is "environmental" and "cultural" in origin or "biogenetic" has a nostalgic flavor, reminiscent of the ancient arguments about heredity and environment. It is obvious that whether we are discussing the facts of physical structure in the animal kingdom or the facts of psychological development in the individual, neither heredity nor environment can operate without the other. It is relevant to ask (a) how early in life and under what circumstances conflicts can be rendered unconscious and thus become sources of neurotic difficulty; and (b) at what stage in development hereditary or genetic influences cease to play a determining role, and how and at what point environmental forces enter the picture. In the argument about this second question one can sometimes detect the irrelevant influence of political bias (v.s. Chapter XX). To attribute to current economic and social stresses the power to generate that subtle, intricate, and universal problem which is known as the neurotic process, is grinding a political axe which should play no role in this issue. It is an attempt to say "what bad economics can cause, good economics can cure." Unfortunately, both assumptions are questionable.

Protagonists of these varying views agree at least verbally on one point, namely that neuroses have their origin in unconscious inner conflicts. Even here, however, disagreements arise since men use the concept of "unconscious" with different connotations. For instance, Adler and Horney seem to mean thoughts and feelings of which we may be unaware, but which are quite close to the surface of consciousness, and which, with little difficulty, can be rendered conscious by direct confrontation. In some respects this is a return to an early analytic assumption, which experience forced Freud to abandon. At the other extreme is the mystical position of Jung, or the sub-depths implications of Klein and the early Rank. These respectively place the unconscious levels of psychological organization on supra-psychological or sub-psychological levels of organization.

The Freudian position stands between these extremes. It places the origins of unconscious processes in that age period in which the child slowly acquires the power of symbolic thought and expression. It recognizes, furthermore, that we are able to perform unconsciously, and often with great economy, every psychological function which we can perform consciously, and that there is a continuous interaction between these two streams of psychological forces and events. This interaction is complicated by a dynamic process which prevents the emergence of unconscious processes into consciousness, except as disguised or "symbolic" acts, thoughts, images and feelings. It is this opposing force which necessitates the use of special technical devices, such as psychoanalysis, in order to bring material from unconscious levels of the personality into consciousness without distortion. Indeed, were it not for this active barrier, there would be no need for any such technique as psychoanalysis. Consequently, no method of investigating or influencing human behavior which fails to deal with this resisting force is, in any meaningful sense of the word, "analytic." This is a dynamic and realistic concept of the nature of unconscious processes, and of their relationship to conscious processes. Yet from this fundamental position there are various divergences, some tacit, some explicit. Sometimes they go to the heart of the entire structure of psychoanalysis, either by denying by implication that there is such an unconscious as psychoanalysis describes, or by regarding the unconscious processes as impotent and insignificant, or else by relegating them to a mysterious, spiritual or sub-psychological world of their own. Thus an even more fundamental problem is interwoven with the question of the age of onset of the neurotic process, to wit, whether neurotic difficulties are due to conscious disappointments, conscious frustrations, conscious deprivations, conscious impulses and conscious conflicts, or whether it is only when such processes become unconscious that they can initiate the neurotic process.

In summarizing these controversies over facts and theories, we can do no better than to paraphrase Robert Waelder's summary at the New School of Social Research in New York City on December 10, 1948. Controversies in analysis are over the biological (instinctual, "genetic") as opposed to the sociological sources of the neuroses; over the deeper or more superficial concept of the nature of unconscious processes;

over the greater or lesser importance of earlier or later ages
in individual developments; over the relative importance
of sexual conflicts and of conflicts over hostility and self-asser-
tion; over whether these conflicts must be unconscious if they
are to produce neuroses, or can exert the same harmful
influence when they are merely conscious reactions to deprivation, frustration, and disappointment.

There are further differences of opinion among analysts
about the relation of analysis to religion and to political,
social and economic change. These have been discussed in
Chapters XVIII and XX.

Controversies over Technique

Special advantages have been claimed for variations in
psychoanalytic technique, but few of these claims have been
adequately tested. Indeed, most of them have not met the
most basic requirement of experimental science: namely, that
when trying out the effects of any changes, only one should
be made at a time, since if several changes are introduced
simultaneously, it becomes impossible to evaluate the effects
of any one of them. With other factors, this makes research
in psychotherapy a laborious and time-consuming task;
which is one reason why there has been so little of it.

Most of the early changes in technique were the steps in a
maturing process, out of which crystallized the essentials of
psychoanalytic technique as we know it today. There have
been several such steps.

(a) The first was the development of the use of free association as the chief technique of exploration (v.s. Chapter
VII). It replaced the initial use of hypnotism and direct
persuasion. These two were abandoned early, leaving behind
a persisting prejudice against further experiments with this
technique. This bias is being resolved now, however, as new
modifications of experimental hypnosis are developing.

When hypnosis first was replaced by the technique of free
association, it was used chiefly in an attempt to explain

symptoms. Soon, however, the free associations were sought to such related phenomena as slips, dreams, and fantasies, until finally free association became the major instrument for the psychoanalytic investigation of the chronology of a whole life history and for the investigation of the personality as a whole.

(b) Next came the gradual recognition of the role of transference and counter-transference and the consequent necessity for preserving the analytic incognito (v.s. Chapter VIII). The goal here was to clarify for the patient the role of unconscious feelings in all of his human relations, by using the unconscious components in his relation to the analyst as an example, at the same time lessening his resistances and facilitating his free associations. From time to time there are analysts who seem to forget the lessons learned in the tough school of analytic frustration, and who abandon all concern with the analysis of transference processes. The fundamental principles involved have already been discussed in Chapters VII and VIII, and need be reviewed here only briefly.

If the analytic incognito is sacrificed or impaired, with it goes all protection of patients from the frailties and fallibility of the analyst; and with it also goes the opportunity for a searching exploration of certain vital areas of the unconscious. This is ancient wisdom. Certainly every inter-personal relationship implies a continuous interplay of conscious and unconscious demands from both sides. This is why it is impossible for any human being to be as objective about relatives and friends as about strangers; and why it is impossible for an analyst to be as objective about a patient with whom he has any extra-analytical ties, as he can be about a patient who has no relation to him except that of an analysand. This automatically precludes any extra-analytical relationships, whether familial, social, or business, during the course of the analysis. Obvious as this seems, some of the adherents of the environmentalist viewpoint argue for free social intercourse between analyst and patients. This, of course, will sometimes give the analyst an opportunity to observe directly the behavior of his patient in current situations, which can surely be illuminating; but the price that is paid for this is exorbitant, since it makes it difficult if not impossible to analyze unconscious components of the transference, and equally difficult to analyze the unconscious components in the patient's conscience, apart from the superimposed standards of the analyst. All of this limits the freedom of the patient's associations; and since free associations are our pathway to unconscious levels of psychological processes, and since informal conversation between analyst and patient requires the selective communications of ordinary speech, such informal contacts slowly but surely bring the essential analytical work to an end.

(c) The next major development was the use of interpretation as a subtle tool for the weakening of resistances, replacing the original naive use of blunt confrontations and symbolic translation.

There was, at first, no recognition of the role played by the forces which obstruct the flow of free associations and the emergence of unconscious material into consciousness. Consequently, early psychoanalytic technique consisted of the direct confrontation of patients with blunt statements of what they were "really" thinking, feeling, or wishing. Conscious behavior, thoughts and feelings were quickly translated into their symbolic unconscious equivalents. Experience soon demonstrated both the limitations and the dangers of this approach; and also the necessity of attacking the resisting forces before attempting to impart any direct insight. It is remarkable that from time to time some analysts will forget even this elementary forward step in the evolution of their technique, and have to learn it over again. This is an issue which is of special significance in relation to all brief forms of psychotherapy, whether analytic or otherwise; since in efforts at brief forms of therapy there is danger of slipping into the error of substituting confrontation for gradual interpretation.

(d) There was an early broadening of the field of analysis from its original concern with symptoms alone to a recon·struction of the chronology of an entire life, and finally to a consideration of the structure of the personality as a whole, with all of its assets and liabilities (currently miscalled "ego-analysis").

It may be worthwhile to keep in mind the ever-present danger of lapsing from the tough task of analyzing to the easier and more gratifying role of moralizing. The analysis of the "personality as a whole", and some of what is called "ego-analysis" sometimes is old-fashioned moralizing in new-fangled, pseudo-analytic terms. This is equally true of some of the talk about "weak" and "strong" egos, which is found in current "orthodox" analytic literature. Name-calling is only name-calling even when done in scientific jargon and by an analyst.

Over each of these natural developmental stages there have been recurring controversies; because, interestingly enough, most of the lessons which have been learned have also been forgotten repeatedly, and have had to be relearned. Ultimately, the effects of this on any science is salutary, since it forces the developing science constantly to re-examine its premises. It is unfortunate only that this retracing of our steps and re-examination of our premises has sometimes been proclaimed to the public as a great new analytic discovery or innovation, when in reality it was a return to something old. This has confused the laity, and has served only to publicize some particular dissenting group for a few brief years.

(e) Another area of controversy over technique centers around the continuity or discontinuity of treatment (v.s. Chapter VI), i.e., whether it is better to continue an analysis indefinitely and without interruptions, or to analyze for short periods with repeated interruptions (as advocated by Alexander, French, *et al.*). There is a related controversy over the duration and frequency of the sessions. These variations involve no fundamental divergence from basic psychoanalytic principles, but their value and limitations have not yet been established or adequately tested (v.i. Section 4).

Only in the analysis of children has the issue of continuity acquired realistic significance. Here two quite opposite schools have developed: one advocating long and continuous analytical treatment, even at an early age; the other defending brief periods of intensive analytic work on the symptomatic upsets of childhood, then waiting for the next flurry of symptoms before carrying treatment further. On theoretical grounds there is something to say on both sides of this question; but there has as yet been no objective comparative study of the long-run results of these two approaches on comparable groups of children. Therefore there are heated words between the two sides, without much light.

(f) In keeping with the evolution of psychoanalytic theory and the divergences which have arisen from time to time, analysts vary in the focus of their attention. Some concentrate primarily on immediate situational problems and daily experiences, some chiefly on various stages of early life; others deal almost exclusively with dreams, or with the quality or "structure" of the personality. It is inevitable that temperamental differences among analysts will be expressed through an enthusiastic over-emphasis of one or another approach. It would seem evident, however, that common sense dictates an attack on a broad front, including symptoms, symptomatic behavior of all kinds, chronology, personality, and finally current problems, omitting none of these components of the total picture from the searching inquiry of the analysis. One can only deplore the efforts of some analysts to make a public crusade for an exclusive emphasis on one or another fragment of the whole.

(g) From time to time analysts have tried to introduce artificial changes in the patient's life, in his work, in his per-

sonal habits, and the like. Such attempts to deliberately
generate tension during the course of treatment have been discussed in some detail in Chapter XI. They are sometimes of
considerable importance in working out the details of treatment, but they are not fundamental departures in analytic
technique. There have been disagreements about the feasi-
bility and efficacy of such attempts (notably as proposed by
Ferenczi); but this has not remained a controversial issue.

(h) Finally, there is the tendency of some deviants to
forget another elementary lesson: namely that the neurotic
process makes it impossible for any neurotic patient, even
with the best will in the world, to accept or follow good counsel and wise advice until the neurotic necessity to be unwise
has been analyzed. Consequently the use of guidance in an
attempt to by-pass the slow, hard labor of analysis usually
fails.

Lurking behind some of these issues is the essential question of whether to analyze at all. Whether or not they realize
and acknowledge it, those who hold that the immediate situation is the source of neurotic difficulty cannot be concerned
about unconscious levels. Therefore, the analysis of unconscious forces seems to them relatively unnecessary. This is
the tacit implication of much of Horney's position. On the
other hand, for those who are convinced that repressed unconscious conflicts are at the root of the neurotic process, no
technical deviations which obstruct or fail to assist in the
uncovering of unconscious material are acceptable.

One must conclude that many of these particular deviations are actually old and not new, backward steps instead of
progress, attempts to solve the problem of the neurosis on too
superficial a level, and in a manner which has already been
tried, and found inadequate, literally centuries ago.

The Frontiers of Research

Where, then, are the advancing frontiers of psychoanalysis? In relation to what analytic problems can we look for

mature research? As in other scientific fields, the significant advances in psychoanalysis are usually those of which the general public hears least. Indeed, many are still blueprints of future investigations which are being planned or are undergoing preliminary trials. Few receive attention in the popular press. This, of course, has great advantages; since anonymity and obscurity make it possible for the investigator to approximate a contemplative and objective spirit.

(a) *Technical Research*

There are researches which bear directly on techniques of treatment, all of them being attempts either to shorten treatment or to make it more effective. Among these are studies of various physiological and psychological procedures by which the free flow of random associative material can be accelerated and maintained. There are studies of methods of manipulating the state of consciousness during analytic sessions, and of inducing and controlling that twilight state which lies between sleep and waking, in which the mind tends automatically to return to its own storm centers. There are experiments on methods of deconditioning, that is of breaking up destructive associative links.

Some of the most important research in the area of technique centers around the problem of *insight*. In Chapter IV, Section 5, we have pointed out that in essence insight is the patient's full understanding of the meaning of his own illness. This depends upon his ability to fill in essential memory gaps both for experience and for feelings, whether recent or remote. This in turn, makes it possible to appreciate the relationship between emotionally charged experiences and the structure and derivation of the personality and of neurotic symptoms. This, however, is a statement of a working hypothesis, and not of a proven fact. Many fundamental problems concerning the role and efficacy of insight remain unsolved. Certain patients are cured almost miraculously through such insight as we have described, while others in spite of similar insight achieve little or no therapeutic relief. The reason for this difference is not yet clear. It is too easy to answer that in the latter case the insight was partial. This is an assumption which is not always verifiable and which usually remains to be investigated and proved. Furthermore, there is always the alternative possibility that insight may not always work the same way. There may also be illnesses in which the retrospective recovery of events and feelings is not effective, and for the relief of which one must in a sense turn back the hands of the clock and relive old experiences as though they were occurring in the present. This sometimes is achieved experimentally in hypnotically induced states of regression to those earlier ages in which the distorting experiences occurred. Nothing final can be said about these problems, except to indicate that the basic hypothesis of therapy through insight is an area of utmost importance for psychoanalytic research.

There are other more superficial but nonetheless significant studies of the effects of variations in details of analytic technique. As we have already indicated, such studies are meaningless unless they take care to vary only one factor at a time. A few examples of these studies will suffice as illustrations: e.g., the sporadic and still inconclusive tests of the effects of varying the frequency and duration of individual sessions; the conduct of analytic sessions in solitude or in the presence of more than one analyst; experimental analysis in groups; the combination of ordinary analytic techniques with analytic processes in groups.

Of basic importance not only to technical but also to clinical research is the development of methods of recording and reproducing the factual and observational data of psychoanalytic psychiatry. No science can progress beyond an elementary qualitative stage until its data can be recorded without distortion, reproduced for subsequent study by more than one observer, and subjected to detailed quantitative as well as qualitative evaluation. The introduction of such methods into the analytic situation creates complex new difficulties. Some analysts feel that these difficulties make it impossible to employ any methods of mechanical recording for the reproduction of analytic experience. Such an attitude would hold up the progress of psychoanalytic science indefinitely; and the use of continuous wire recordings and of sound film is slowly being tried out, both for investigative and for teaching purposes. This is the first step towards a comprehensive qualitative and quantitative analysis of random associative material. The entire apparatus of modern statistical methodology and machinery will some day be brought to bear on these problems. This, however, waits upon the development of the proper type of specialized research institutes for the study of the psychological and physiological manifestations of the neurotic process.

(b) *Clinical Research*

There have as yet been no systematic comparisons of the efficacy of any forms of analysis with different neurotic constellations, none at least which are statistically adequate, nor which have been followed over a sufficiently long time. As a matter of fact, in order to carry on a comparative study of therapeutic results, it will be necessary to meet certain fundamental prerequisites, none of which are available today.

(1) In the first place, psychoanalysis must no longer be confined to the field of private practice, in which it was born and nurtured. It was no accident that analysis started in this way. For various reasons this had to be; but further scientific progress is no longer possible under these conditions. The affluent can no longer serve effectively as the guinea-pig for humanity. Endowments are needed to subsidize psychoanalytic studies in hospitals and medical schools, in educational institutions from the nursery school through the university, in social agencies and courts, in industry, and in special institutes for research in psychoanalytic psychiatry.

Such research institutes must be built around treatment centers where selected types of neurotic illness can be analyzed without considering the ability of any individual to pay, so that systematic cultural-anthropological, socio-economic, and psychoanalytic studies can be made on statistically adequate samples, both random and selected, and followed up over an adequate length of time.

(2) Comparative studies of the responses of different neurotic constellations to the analytic process require as a preliminary step a careful re-examination and perhaps a basic reshuffling of currently accepted nosological categories. Such studies can be made only if they are carried on conjointly with neuro-physiologists, clinical psychologists, sociologists, cultural anthropologists and social workers; because this study will require the evaluation of physiological as well as psychological forces which produce and shape the neurotic process and their quantitative estimation; and these in turn must be related to the cultural mores and the socio-economic forces in which the neurotic process has been developed.

(3) Furthermore, with the aid of clinical psychology we need to develop new testing instruments, designed to provide us with quantitative data on the relative roles of conscious and unconscious processes in the lives of the patients who are under investigation, before, during and after treatment. It will not be possible to make precise studies either of the etiological process or of the therapeutic process until such techniques as these have been developed. Current qualitative indices must be supplemented by quantitative tools, which ultimately will be usable in practical clinical work as well as in research. Such studies are needed also to provide us with a clearer definition of the relationship between the symptomatic neuroses and the characterological neuroses, with special attention to that most difficult of all challenges to the analyst, namely, the need to induce characterological changes (v.s. Chapter XVII, Section 3).

(c) *Theoretical Research*

Priority among theoretical studies is given to the need for weeding and pruning the overgrown garden of analytic concepts and terms. This is important in any verbal science which, like psychoanalysis, has developed swiftly and simultaneously in scattered lands and different tongues. The multiplication of partially overlapping and partially redundant concepts and terms is a source of great confusion in psychoanalytic thinking, and tends to obstruct its further growth.

Areas of research in theory are almost infinite in their possibilities. There is not a single aspect of psychoanalytic theory which cannot be subjected to objective tests for verification or qualification. One might give as an example the cinematographic studies by Spitz of the effect on infants of separation from the mother for varying periods of time and at varying ages. This is a first step towards an objective study of one of the basic problems of human development. The next step would be to trace in those same infants the later fate of these experiences as manifested in articulate and inarticulate play, in conscious and unconscious fantasies, in physiology, in dreams, in personality, and finally in subsequent symptomatic history.

Analytical studies of the cultural anthropology of the neuroses are waiting to be made, on our own doorsteps. It is dismaying that the incidence in our own population of not a single neurotic symptom has been established, much less that of the subtler neurotic personality distortions. We do not know what the incidence is in relation to age, economic or educational groups, religious affiliations, national origins, nor in relation to population-density, occupations, or the like. This lack of factual data should make us skeptical when we hear positive statements about the relative roles in the evolution of neurosis of cultural and environmental factors on the one hand as opposed to genetic and biological forces on the other.

Heated arguments which anticipate factual information can never be more than an expression of bias.

This then is another area of research into fundamental theoretical concepts and working hypotheses, which demands the coordinated efforts of sociologists, cultural anthropologists, clinical psychologists and psychoanalytic psychiatrists, studying random samples of all elements of our population. Such a project would include, naturally, a re-examination of the entire story of psycho-sexual development, by teams of scientists who are adequately trained and mature enough to correct the errors made by the naive methods of Kinsey and his co-workers.

We do not even know today what correlation, if any, there is between the size of families and the incidence and development of neuroses. Data are needed on the variations in psychological development which arise out of different types of family constellations: e.g., family size, age and sex differences among children, separations from one or another parent at different age periods, the effects of illness, accident and death, and the type of early birth and early nourishment. All of these variables and many others must some day be studied in terms of their influence on ultimate psychological development.

Finally, a test of the value of preventive psychiatry remains to be made. This would involve the selection of a stable and representative community in which every facility of modern psychiatry would be made available to an adequate random sample of the young couples who were about to marry or about to have children, providing psychiatric education and psychiatric treatment both for the children and for the adults. After ten or fifteen years these children could then be compared to a control group from the same community with respect to their adjustments in homes, schools, playground, sports, and community as a whole, and as to the morbidity and mortality rates among them.

This is by no means an exhaustive list of all possible areas of psychoanalytic research. It is merely an effort to indicate some of the frontiers, some of the directions in which we may look for basic progress, not merely in theory, not in minute variations in details of analytic procedure, and certainly not in abandoning established fundamental principles. These are areas in which research can and should be carried out by unfettered scientists, who would owe no immediate service either to students or to patients, but who would be psychologically free to pursue uncharted courses to unexpected and unpredictable truths. This is the way of scientific progress.

Some Additional Comments

Every healthy science grows through controversy and research; but the areas of controversy and the areas of research are not identical. Moreover, controversies tend to be noisy, while significant research is more likely to be quiet and retiring. There are disagreements over which aspects of psychoanalytic theory best illuminate behavior, and which aspects provide effective instruments in the attempt to help people. Some theoretical developments prove to be effective levers; others are relatively impotent. This does not, in and of itself, prove that any theory is either true or false. The original, modest goal of psychoanalysis was to ameliorate the symptoms of illness. There is a growing realization that symptomatic relief can endure only if at the same time the therapeutic process alters those personality qualities out of which illness grows. This, however, is a more difficult goal. Consequently, psychoanalysis has been forced to undertake the formidable task of changing the personality of the patient in order to relieve the neurotic pain to which the personality gives rise.

There is controversy over whether or not the evolution of the neurotic process is determined predominantly by the idiosyncracies of individual experience in early life or by cultural stereotypes, and over how these two factors interact. There are controversies over the extent to which variations in human neurophysiology and neurobiochemistry determine the vulnerability to developmental distortions, and whether these, in turn, arise spontaneously or in response to the varied stresses of life. There are controversies over whether physiological processes are themselves alterable by psychological influences alone, and, conversely, whether it is possible to exert a combination of physiological, pharmacological, and psychological influences in the effort to alter personality and behavior. All of these are valid areas for investigation and for free debate. Such debate is valuable when it spurs men on to research. Unfortunately, it sometimes becomes a wordy substitute for research, especially when the debates center around trivial, verbal, and ephemeral issues. This does little harm to scientists other than those whose energies are consumed in trivial struggles. But when such debates are conducted in public, they breed confusion because the press tends to depict one side as completely right and the other as completely wrong. This is more dramatic than it is accurate, since most such positions are complex mixtures of right and wrong which must be carefully sorted out and clarified. Consequently, the premature taking of sides in public rarely adds to clarity, either for the scientist who is investigating the field or for the public which is waiting eagerly for knowledge and help.

APPENDIX

The American Psychoanalytic Association is located at 1 East 57th Street, New York 22, N. Y. (telephone, OXford 7-3171). Mrs. Helen Fischer is acting Executive Secretary. Doctors Bertram D. Lewin and Helen Ross are consultants on psychoanalytic education to the institutes and training centers which are affiliated with the American Psychoanalytic Association.

The institutes and training centers currently recognized (as of July, 1960) by the American Psychoanalytic Association are listed below, in alphabetical order:

Baltimore Psychoanalytic Institute
    821 North Charles Street, Baltimore 1, Md.
Boston Psychoanalytic Society and Institute, Inc.
    15 Commonwealth Avenue, Boston 16, Mass.
Chicago Institute for Psychoanalysis
    664 North Michigan Avenue, Chicago 11, Ill.
Cleveland Psychoanalytic Training Center
    School of Medicine, Western Reserve University, Hanna
    Pavilion, University Hospitals
    2040 Abington Road, Cleveland 6, Ohio
Columbia University Psychoanalytic Clinic
    Columbia Presbyterian Medical Center
    722 West 168th Street, New York 32, N. Y.
Division of Psychoanalytic Education, State University of
    New York, College of Medicine at New York City
    606 Winthrop Street, Brooklyn 3, N. Y.
Institute of the Philadelphia Association for Psychoanalysis
    122 South 18th Street, Philadelphia 3, Penna.
Institute for Psychoanalytic Medicine of Southern California
    9756 Wilshire Boulevard, Beverly Hills, Calif.
Los Angeles Institute for Psychoanalysis
    344 North Bedford Drive, Beverly Hills, Calif.

New Orleans Psychoanalytic Training Center, Inc.
  1328 Aline Street, New Orleans 15, La.
New York Psychoanalytic Institute
  247 East 82nd Street, New York 28, N. Y.
Philadelphia Psychoanalytic Institute
  1636 Walnut Street, Philadelphia 3, Penna.
Psychoanalytic Training Center of Detroit
  1242 Maccabees Building, Detroit 2, Mich.
San Francisco Psychoanalytic Institute
  2380 Sutter Street, San Francisco 15, Calif.
Seattle Psychoanalytic Training Center
  4033 East Madison Street, Seattle 2, Wash.
Topeka Institute for Psychoanalysis
  3617 West Sixth Avenue, Topeka, Kans.
Washington Psychoanalytic Institute
  1720 M Street N.W., Washington 6, D.C.
Western New England Institute for Psychoanalysis
  340 Whitney Avenue, New Haven 11, Conn.

BIBLIOGRAPHY

The following listing comprises various other articles and books by the author which he considers useful for supplementary reading on the subject. They are arranged according to their relevancy to the topics treated in each chapter.

Chapter III

"The Concept of Normality and Neurosis," in *Psychoanalysis and Social Work* (ed M. Heiman), Chapter I (pp. 3–4). New York: International Universities Press, 1953.

"The Fundamental Nature of the Distinction Between Normality and Neurosis," *Psychoanalytic Quarterly*, Vol. 23, No. 2 (1954), pp. 167–204.

Neurotic Distortion of the Creative Process. Porter Lectures, Series 22. Lawrence, Kansas: University of Kansas Press, 1958.

"The Neurotic Potential, the Neurotic Process, and the Neurotic State," *U.S. Armed Forces Medical Journal*, Vol. 2, No. 1 (January, 1951), pp. 1–12.

"The Neurotic Process as the Focus of Physiological and Psychoanalytic Research," *Journal of Mental Science* (London), Vol. 104, No. 435 (April, 1958), pp. 518–536.

"Some Implications for Psychoanalysis of Modern Concepts of the Organization of the Brain," *Psychoanalytic Quarterly*, Vol. 22, No. 1 (January, 1953), pp. 21–68.

Chapter VII

Neurotic Distortion of the Creative Process, op. cit.

"Neurotic Process as Focus of Physiological and Psychoanalytic Research," *op. cit.*

"Problems and Techniques of Psychoanalytic Validation and Progress," in *Psychoanalysis as Science* (ed. E. Pumpian-Mindlin), pp. 46–124. Hixon Fund Lectures of the California Institute of Technology. Stanford, Calif.: Stanford University Press, 1952.

"Psychoanalysis as a Basic Science," in *Twenty Years of Psychoanalysis* (ed. F. Alexander and H. Ross), pp. 120–145. New York: W. W. Norton & Company, 1953.

"The Use of Psychoanalysis as a Research Tool," *Psychiatric Research Reports 6*, American Psychiatric Association, October, 1956, pp. 112–136.

Chapter XV

"The Objective Evaluation of Psychotherapy," Round Table, 1948, *American Journal of Orthopsychiatry*, Vol. 19, No. 3 (July, 1949), pp. 463–467, 488–491.

"Problems in Clinical Research," Round Table, 1946, *American Journal of Orthopsychiatry*, Vol. 17, No. 2 (April, 1947), pp. 196–203, 222, 230.

"Research in Psychotherapy," Round Table, 1947, *American Journal of Orthopsychiatry*, Vol. 18, No. 1 (January, 1948), pp. 92–95.

"Some Unsolved Problems of Psychoanalytic Psychotherapy," in *Progress in Psychotherapy* (ed. F. Fromm-Reichmann and J. L. Moreno), pp. 87–102. New York: Grune & Stratton, 1956.

"Symposium: Evaluation of Therapeutic Results" (with C. P. Oberndorf, P. Greenacre, and others), *International Journal of Psychoanalysis*, Vol. 29 (1948), Part 1, pp. 7–20.

Chapter XVI

"A Pilot Study of Psychoanalytic Practice in the U.S.: With Suggestions for Future Studies," *Psychiatry*, Vol. 13, No. 2 (1950), pp. 227–245.

Chapter XVII

"Freud's Legacy to Human Freedom," *Proceedings of the Rudolph Virchow Medical Society*, Vol. 15 (1956), pp. 34–48.

"The Neurosis Wears a Mask," in *Moments of Personal Discovery* (ed. R. M. MacIver), Chapter 3 (pp. 27–36). New York: Harper & Brothers for the Institute for Religious and Social Studies, 1952.

"New Approaches to Old Problems," *Child Study*, Vol. 27, No. 3 (Summer, 1950), pp. 73–74.

"Psychiatry in Relation to Freedom and Authority," *Journal of Religious Thought* (Washington, D.C.: Howard University Press), Vol. 9, No. 1 (Autumn–Winter, 1951–52), pp. 40–48.

Chapter XIX

"The Disintegrating Impact of 'Modern' Life on the Family in America and Its Explosive Repercussions," in *Emotional Forces in the Family* (ed. Samuel Liebman), Chapter 9 (pp. 135–149). Philadelphia, Pa.: J. B. Lippincott Co., 1959.

"Dr. Kinsey and the Medical Profession" (a review of *Sexual Behavior in the Human Female* by Kinsey *et al.*), *Psychosomatic Medicine*, Vol. 17, No. 3 (May–June, 1955), pp. 172–184.

"Psychiatric Implications of the Kinsey Report" (a review of *Sexual*

Behavior in the Human Male by Kinsey *et al.*), *Psychosomatic Medicine*, Vol. 10, No. 2 (1948), pp. 95–106.

"Psychoanalysis and Marriage: Practical and Theoretical Issues," in *Neurotic Interaction in Marriage* (ed. V. W. Eisenstein), Chapter 2 (pp. 10–43). New York: Basic Books, 1956.

Chapter XX

"Is Preventive Psychiatry Possible?" *Daedalus* (Journal of American Academy of Arts & Sciences), Vol. 88, No. 4 (Fall, 1959), pp. 646–668.

"Freud's Legacy to Human Freedom," *op. cit.*

"Pavlov, Freud and Soviet Psychiatry," *Behavioral Science*, Vol. 4, No. 1 (January, 1959), pp. 29–34.

"Social Forces and the Neurotic Process," in *Explorations in Social Psychiatry* (ed. Alexander H. Leighton), Chapter 3 (pp. 77–99). New York: Basic Books, 1957.

Chapter XXI

"Freud's Legacy to Human Freedom," *op. cit.*

"Pavlov, Freud and Soviet Psychiatry," *op. cit.*

"Psychoanalysis—Costly Fad or Boon to Mankind?" (reply to Monsignor Fulton J. Sheen), *New York Herald Tribune*, April 20, 1947, Section 11, p. 7.

Chapter XXII

"Pilot Study of Psychoanalytic Practice in U.S. . . . ," *op. cit.*

"The Search for Maturity in Pre-Professional Education," *Clinical Research*, Vol. VII, No. 2 (April, 1959), pp. 177–183.

Chapter XXIII

"The Need for a New Subdiscipline in the Medical Profession," *Archives of Neurology and Psychiatry*, Vol. 78, No. 3 (September, 1957), pp. 283–293.

"The Pros and Cons of a New Profession: A Doctorate in Medical Psychology," *Texas Reports on Biology and Medicine*, Vol. 12, No. 3 (Fall, 1954), pp. 692–737.

Chapter XXIV

"The Problem of Maturity in Psychiatric Research," *Journal of Medical Education*, Vol. 28, No. 10 (October, 1953), pp. 11–27.

Chapter XXV

"An Institute for Basic Research in Psychiatry," *Bulletin of the Menninger Clinic*," Vol. 20, No. 6 (November, 1956), pp. 281–287.

"The Investigation of the Pharmacology of Psychological Processes: Some Methodologic Considerations from the Point of View of Clinical Psychoanalysis," in *Psychopharmacology* (ed. Harry H. Pennes), Chapter XII (pp. 302–315). New York: Paul B. Hoeber, 1958.

"Neurotic Process as Focus of Physiological and Psychoanalytic Research," *op. cit.*

"Problems and Techniques of Psychoanalytic Validation and Progress," *op. cit.*

"Psychoanalysis as Basic Science," *op. cit.*

"Psychoanalysis and Psychopharmacology," *Psychiatric Research Reports 9*, American Psychiatric Association, March, 1958, pp. 61–67.

"Research into the Process of Supervision in Psychoanalysis," *Psychoanalytic Quarterly*, Vol. XXVII, No. 2 (April, 1958), pp. 226–236.

"Some Unsolved Problems of Psychoanalytic Psychotherapy," *op. cit.*

"Use of Psychoanalysis as Research Tool," *op. cit.*